2020 Creative Writing Short Stories

A Collection of Short Stories
Written by Members
Of the Atria Willow Glen
Creative Writing Group

The design of this book was performed by Elvet E. Moore, an ATRIA resident, using the Creatspace Personal Computer Publishing System provided by Amazon.com.

Foreword

The Atria Willow Glen Creative Writing Group meets weekly with members writing short stories which are shared with the other members at each meeting. To help stimulate the newer members to write a variety of short stories, the leader often passes out various clips known as writing prompts to be followed by them.

In addition, once a month Martha Engber comes to the meeting in Atria to assist all of the Creative Writers. She teaches Creative Writing at the San Jose University, and is very helpful in providing proper writing solutions for all of our residents to follow.

During the peak of the Covid-19 Virus Activity, the resident members and Martha did not meet at Atria together as a group. However, the members did continue to meet separately and write Creative Writing Stories, which they later shared with each other when the class resumed.

Since its inception, the group has published six different books containing numerous short stories. This seventh book contains stories which the members felt represented some of the best of their works. By collecting them together they are able to share them with you.

Table of Contents

Table of Contents (Page 2)

Table of Contents (Page 3) (Concluded)

How Green was that Probe – Five Chapter Story

Tom Brandt Stories

My Dad's Advice

By Tom Brandt
Submitted on April, 2020

Incoming freshmen at Princeton could not participate in any extra-curricular activities for the fall term, for the adjustment to collegiate life required concentration. However, in January, when the spring term began, I attended a recruiting meeting at the

Theatre Intima (that's a French expression meaning "small theater").

I signed on as a switchboard operator for the upcoming production of *King Lear*. This turned into a monumental production in a tiny 300-seat theater which had a thrust stage and virtually no wing space to store scenery. Thus, the set designer created a unit set—that is, a single arrangement of platforms to create levels that did not change throughout the play.

The scene changes were accomplished by shifting the lighting around to different parts of the set. Thus we switchboard operators were an intimate part of creating the illusion. In today's world this sort of thing is programed into computers and the lighting team of one person merely moves a mouse around, whereas in those days, we had to raise and lower the lights by adjusting individual dimmer handles. It took two of us to manipulate the array of two-dozen dimmer handles, and we had more than one hundred cues and lighting changes during the three-hour production.

I became enchanted by the art of play production and began to spend more time building scenery than studying. I became a skilled scene carpenter and general mechanic. The reckoning came, however, when I pulled a "D" in freshman Physics. Mother was aghast and she launched into one of her special guilt trips over the fact that I had nearly failed a course— especially a Physics course.

Dad was more measured. I realize in retrospect that he was more interested in what I had learned about life. He actually encouraged me to continue with the theater, but to do a better job of time management. He was not interested in academic excellence, but instead what I was learning in the broader sense.

In the end, he gave me great advice. I continued my bipolar career by maintaining what we called at the time a "Gentleman's B" academically, and went on to become the Technical Director of the Triangle Club in my senior year.

The Triangle Club was then totally extra-curricular. The club had its own theater, the McCarter, which seated 1,200 souls and had a fully equipped stage. It produced an original musical comedy all written and composed by undergraduates. We had a cast of fifty and an orchestra of fifteen, two property managers, plus my team of six stage crews. We hired a professional director, a choreographer, and a music arranger, but otherwise we did it all by ourselves, including building and painting all of the scenery.

As Technical Director, I was responsible to see that the physical attributes of the show were ready to go at curtain time. The show opened in Princeton in early December, and then during the Christmas holiday the show toured the United States. We played in New York, in Baltimore, in Washington, in Cleveland, in

Pittsburgh, in Cincinnati, and in St. Louis, to name a few. We traveled by train, which consisted of two Pullman cars for the cast and crew and one baggage car that held the lights, props, scenery, and costumes for the performances. We generally arrived in town before lunch, and then spent the afternoon hanging the show.

The performances were all one-night stands followed by the Triangle Ball—a black tie affair. The stage crew always got to the party late, because we had to strike the show and pack it into the baggage car before we could strip off our stinking coveralls, shower, and change into party clothes. I wore out my first tuxedo with the wear and tear of my three tours.

In the end, my Dad was right. I learned so much taking that show on the road. I had just turned 21 and here I was directing the efforts of men who had spent their lives backstage in scenery, properties, lighting, wardrobe, and flying the great drops.

All of this transpired under the watchful eyes of the local fire marshals and house managers. The railroad crew had parked the baggage car on a siding convenient to off-load the baggage car by day and repack it after the show. The railroad folks needed the baggage car to be ready to roll no later than 2 AM for it to be part of the consist for the next stop on the tour.

Our baggage car was filled with drops, flats, and two electrical switchboards, four or five cases of lights, and about ten wardrobe trunks, among other assorted gadgets. One cannot fit a forty-foot drop onto a fifteen-foot pick-up truck.

We had a hard deadline to meet. The curtain must go up at the appointed time. There was a whole paid audience out there waiting for the show, and there can be no delays. The Technical Director is responsible to see that the lights are in place and focused, the drops and curtains are hung, and the miscellaneous props and scenery are in place before curtain time.

I learned, among all other things, to respect deadlines. None of this would ever be covered in an engineering curriculum. At graduation, I felt that I had majored in Theatrical Production and got my BSE from Princeton on the side.

Dave's Repose

By Tom Brandt
Submitted on April, 2020

Dave headed straight for his favorite hidden grove—a place he discovered one day while wandering aimlessly through the familiar forest. The gurgle of the creek told him he was close. Then with one last push through the bracken, he was into the tiny glade he loved. It was his private place to think.

He settled against the roots and trunk of the giant blue spruce. Its lower trunk was covered with moss that cushioned all the sharp points. This part of the forest was so dense that moss grew all the way around its trunk. No telling North by the moss in here. That was a bit of unreliable folklore, anyhow, but especially so in deep cover.

Dave liked it here because there were no sounds of human origin. The creek burbled its way down the hill. The gentle breeze created whispers in the needles of the spruce and pine trees. Chickadees and warblers sang their merry songs. Once in a while a squirrel rustled through the fallen leaves. One day last week he heard a larger creature crunching through the undergrowth. He worried for a few moments until he spied the groundhog shuffling its way across the forest floor.

Quiet—this place was certainly not. Still, without human distractions, he could work on his problem—the natural sounds of other living things living out their lives while helping him to relax and focus on his dilemma.

A tiny warbler had found a twig that it wanted, probably for a nest. The twig was as long as the bird and the wee creature struggled with its prize. The twig finally gave way and snapped off a piece half as long as the original. Whether by plan or by chance this is what the warbler needed. So it happily took to the air with its shortened prize.

Dave sat in awe of the mental process of the tiny creature. He realized that was his problem, too. He was working on the whole situation at once, but he needed to break it into smaller component parts and solve them one at a time, while keeping a weather eye on the main event. He whispered "Thank You" in the direction the warbler had flown, gathered his gear, and with a light heart, walked home with the outline of his new approach formulating in his mind.

Virginia Braxton Stories

Magellan

By Virginia Braxton
Submitted on November, 2019

"Don't you dare touch that!"

"But, Mom...!"

"I said, Do. Not. Touch. That!" Carol reiterated.

"Mom, it's for school!" Kevin protested.

"Explain please."

"It's for show and tell."

"Take something else for show and tell."

"But it has to be something that shows off our family history."

"OK...What are you going to say about it?"

"This is the boat my great grandpa David went in around the world with Magellan."

"Kevin, think. You're holding it in your hand. Could your great grandpa fit into that?"

"Well, it's just like Magellan's boat, but tiny instead."

"Good. Now who was Magellan?"

"He went all the way around the world in a very slow boat, but in the middle he was eaten by cannibals."

"Let's untangle that a bit. We know he was killed half way around the world, but we don't know for sure about the cannibals. How can you say that?"

"Magellan had a very slow boat and he started to go around the world, but he was killed by cannibals, and his boat went the rest of the way without him."

"OK...Kevin. Magellan lived before there were cars or airplanes—before there was even America. Why does this family care about him?"

"Great grandpa was with him!"

"No, dear, I'm not that old. Great grandpa David and some friends wished they could have gone with Magellan, so they built a ship just like his and wore his kind of clothes, and sailed to the same places he did."

"Like when Dad puts on that grey uniform and talks about damn Yankees?"

"Yes, dear, it's called reenacting," Carol sighed. "I'll wrap the model boat so it doesn't get broken on the way to school. Now, can you tell me why Magellan is part of this family's history?"

"Great grandpa wanted to go with Magellan, but there were no cars then, so they built a boat like his and sailed after him.

"But he wasn't eaten by cannibals."

Stand by Your Man

By Virginia Braxton
Submitted on March, 2020

Martha sat in the limo struggling with a kaleidoscope of emotions—numbness, apprehension, humiliation, and anger.

Talk about objectification! Brad's handlers had measured the length of her skirt, stuffed her bra, teased her hair, and glued false eyelashes on her so she would be more appealing when she stood beside him and performed the "I'll Stand by my Man" speech they wanted her to make.

She remembered when she and Brad were younger. They had met in college and she couldn't believe that anyone so handsome and charming would choose her. And it had lasted—sort of. They had married when they graduated from college and moved to Boston, where Brad had a scholarship to Harvard Law School, but the financial aid wasn't quite enough for them to live on.

They had agreed that she should get a job, and after Brad graduated it would be her turn to go to school. Her job had worked out surprisingly well. She was planning to be a marine biologist and found a position as an aide to Professor Gonsalves. He was a genuine teacher and told her of the wonderful sea creatures he had seen, where he had grown up in Goa on the shore of the Arabian Gulf.

The summer she had spent working with him at Woods Hole was the highpoint in her life so far, although she had decided to specialize in tropical creatures, and the waters off Cape Cod were not exactly tropical.

She remembered now, rather wryly, that she had believed Brad each time he had given her a reason why he could not come down for the weekend. Well, she wasn't that naive anymore.

Before Brad had graduated she had begun applying for formal study at various universities, but Brad had come home one night and announced that he had accepted a new job with a prestigious law firm in Chicago, and they were going to move there. She had cried and cried, but Brad said she was just being an emotional woman and that they would have a good life there together.

At least Professor Gonsalves had written a recommendation for her, so she could get a good job at the local Chicago Aquarium, but she spent most of her time talking to eight-year-olds, rather than talking with researchers.

Brad flourished in Chicago. He was rising rapidly in the firm, and was increasingly interested in the intricacies of local politics. He had been ecstatic when he had been invited to have dinner with the chairman of the slating committee. However, her mother had died suddenly and the funeral was in Florida scheduled for the very same evening.

Brad had refused to go with her, saying that he might not have another chance with the chairman and she had said that surely the politico would understand a death in the family, but Brad refused to try to reschedule and she had gone to Florida alone.

Their anniversary, her birthday, and Valentine's Day were always remembered, but the presents were always generic, like a day at the spa, or a piece of jewelry, and were nothing like that silly stuffed gorilla Brad had given her when they were dating.

She suspected that the dates were in a computer and Brad's secretary had taken care of the details for him. It was years since he'd handwritten a gift card for her. As for her, it had become hard to talk with him, let alone choose a gift for him that meant something.

He never seemed interested in anything but his political future. He certainly never did *pro bono* work or went to a community gathering, unless his handlers told him to do so. And now along came this latest crisis.

When the picture of him holding a baby surfaced, she initially thought that holding babies is part of the politician's trade, although she thought the look on his face was unusually sappy. Then the DNA was leaked and she knew that the child was his.

His handlers demanded that she perform a "Stand by Your Man" speech. She was told that to make a mistake is human and Brad is (all too) human. As she was getting out of the car and being led onto the platform, the handler whispered, "Remember now, don't rub your eyes, and don't mess up your eyelashes."

Something suddenly coalesced inside Martha as she took her place on the platform. She could see that all the TV stations had crews there, as well as the print media. She studied them without listening to Brad as he performed his part of the act. Then the emcee said, "And now a word from Brad's wife," while he handed her the microphone.

Martha took it and looking straight at the reporters said, "I was brought here and told to make a speech about "Standing by my Man." However I'm not going to do that. I'm going to vote for his opponent instead."

The emcee made a grab for the microphone, but Martha waved it out of his reach and asked him, "Are you going to assault me here on camera?" At the same time she saw the handler signaling the sound technician, so she said, "If you cut off my mike, the reporters all have their own mikes anyway and will record whatever I have to say.

"And what I have to say is this. Brad will not be a good representative for the community because he doesn't give a damn about anyone but himself. He has made no sustained commitment of any kind to community service. He has never done a lick of *pro bono* work. In private he makes fun of anyone who hasn't gone to Harvard, including me. He has no position that he really believes in—he is simply a mouthpiece for the machine. We'd be better off voting for the kid who is running against him, and that's what I'm going to do."

She turned and climbed down from the platform. The reporters jostled and shouted questions at her, but she had nothing more to say. The handlers got her into the limo as quickly as they could. She looked back and saw Brad standing silently on the platform.

In the limo's comparative quiet she thought to herself. "The first thing I'll do is get the locks changed, maybe this afternoon. Then I'll ask Tom Grady for the name of a good divorce lawyer. And then I'm going to see if I can wrangle a place on the expedition to the Great Barrier Reef. I can always get an absentee ballot there."

17

A Night to Remember

By Virginia Braxton
Submitted on March, 2020

Jean's first thought that morning was "tonight's the prom." She wasn't as excited about it as she would have been if they had stayed in Canton and she could have finished high school there. She'd cried buckets when Dad said they were going to have to move.

He said he wasn't going to be one of those men who weren't around, even though they sent money back home. They were a family unit and were going to stay together, no matter what. So now they were living all on top of each other in a double-wide trailer on the edge of the oil field where dad worked.

Tim had asked her, and he wasn't a bad date. At least the other girls wouldn't tease her about him. And he had asked her to dinner at a restaurant in town before the prom. He didn't have a car, but her Dad had promised to drive them, (probably, she thought, to keep an eye on them.)

Mom had found a store that featured slightly used prom dresses, and she let her pick one out. The one she chose was a filmy fabric in a sort of sea turquoise with sequins here and there, and Mom found some

19

shoes to go with it. She'd hardly recognized herself when she saw herself in the fitting room full length mirror. She wished the trailer had a full length mirror like this one.

She did a double take when she got out of bed that morning and saw her Dad had dressed for work. "Dad," she exclaimed, "Have you forgotten? You said you were going to drive Tim and me to the prom tonight! Why are you getting ready for work?"

"I'm sorry, dear," said her Dad. "The new foreman wants me to work the noon till 8:00 pm shift just this once, and he'll pay me double-time. I couldn't say no to that."

"But you promised to drive Tim and me! How are we going to get there?"

"I was worried about that too," her Dad said. "So, I've made arrangements for my friend, John Black, to drive you. He is working the first shift."

"You arranged for *Red Johnny* to drive us to the prom? I'll never live that one down. I'd be better off staying at home," she said.

Her Dad stiffened. "Jean Elizabeth Carpenter," he said in a quiet voice, "You are never, ever, to speak of him that way again. He is John Black and you are to refer to him as Mr. Black!"

"But everybody calls him *Red Johnny,* because he's half Indian!"

"I don't care what other people do. You are to call him Mr. Black. Do you think I'd trust my little girl to just anybody? He's my friend, and besides, he saved my life."

Jean sat down suddenly. "What happened, Daddy?"

"Oh, Lord," her father said. "That slipped out. Your mother and I weren't going to tell you, because we didn't want you to worry too much. But there's no getting away from it now. These oil field jobs are so risky."

"But, what happened? Was that the day you came home extra dirty and you and mom were so quiet? I heard at school that there'd been an accident and a foreman had been killed."

"You are right on all three counts, Jean. The man who was killed was the foreman of the team I was on."

"Well, where does Red—I mean Mr. Black—come into all of this?"

"We were all on the rig working, when out of nowhere John started shouting, "Get off! Get off! It's going to blow! The foreman cursed and tried to shut him up. He said he'd have John fired for insubordination.

"The rest of us started scrambling, and John tried to haul the foreman with us, but the stupid"—her dad caught himself before he said what he thought of the foreman. "Anyway, John got himself down and was just at the safety point when it blew." The foreman didn't have a chance. John asked us not to tell what he had done because, after all, we had disobeyed the foreman, and we all did what John had asked.

"Jean, don't you tell anyone either, do you understand me? But, enough about that."

Jean's dad took a deep breath and said, "Now, you and Tim are going to ride in style. Most people don't know it, but John has a big old Cadillac, a classic, with great big fins and without a scratch on it. He keeps it under cover and it's beautifully polished, and he only takes it out when he's going to old car shows. He's going to get it out and drive you and Tim to the dance. It will be a sensation."

Jean realized that she didn't have a choice, and that Dad didn't realize that cars were a boy thing anyway. Well, Tim would be happy at least.

* * *

Dad had already left for work when Mom helped her dress. She let her use some perfume, piled up Jean's hair, and gave her a special pair of earrings that went with the beautiful gown.

Mr. Black had already picked up Tim when he arrived in the humongous Cadillac. Tim got out, handed her a corsage without ceremony, and said, "Look at this car! Isn't it fabulous?"

Just as they were about to get into the car, Mom handed her an umbrella, and said, "Here dear, take this. I see some clouds, and it would be a pity to get that beautiful dress wet."

Tim ushered her into the back seat over which a huge animal skin had been thrown. He climbed in beside her and went on talking car talk with Mr. Black. Jean fingered the soft fur of the pelt on which they sat.

Jean couldn't get excited about the car or take part in the talk, so she looked out the window. Mom was right. The clouds were piling up. Mr. Black kept taking glances out the window too, as the sky became darker and darker. They saw it at the same time—a funnel cloud!

"OK," said Mr. Black. "We'll have to take shelter and there's damn little of it out here. This car's no good in a tornado. Best I can think of is that railroad overpass where the main line crosses the old spur line.

"Now, while I'm driving, you two get ready to take cover. Tim, pull the buffalo skin off the seat now, so we can take it with us. Jean, there's a lantern and a first aid kit behind my seat. Pull them out now and take them with you."

He floored the gas pedal. As the car rocketed along, Jean and Tim bounced against each other while they wrestled with the heavy buffalo skin. They were able to pile it in front of Tim, and Jean was able to grab the emergency supplies. Rain drummed on the car and debris hit against the windshield as Mr. Black turned the car into a field and drove straight to the overpass. They skidded to a stop. Mr. Black jumped out, pulled them out of the car, flung Jean into a ditch with Tim on top of her, and threw himself and the buffalo robe over them all.

Jean was never able to put into words what she felt as the tornado passed by. After a bit, Mr. Black threw back the buffalo skin, sat up, and said, "That was a close one. How are you two?"

Jean was muddy and shaken, but had no visible injuries. Tim had a gash on his leg, which was bleeding.

"Jean, you still have the first aid kit and the lantern? Good girl." Mr. Black applied ointment around Tim's wound, put a pad on it, and held it in place with strips he tore from Jean's gown.

"Now, to get us out of here," he said. "The tornado took my car. You stay here where there's at least a little bit of shelter."

It was still raining, but not as hard when he grabbed the lantern and went into the muddy field. He turned the lantern on and shined it straight up in a steady beam, and then quickly turned it on and off as an SOS signal. At first it looked faint against the sky, but as dusk fell it showed up more. Then he shouted, "Someone's coming!"

Jean, Tim, and Mr. Black piled into the rescue vehicle. The driver was talking on his radio. "Yeah, I've got Steve Chapman's little girl, Jean, with me and Clancy's boy, Tim. Tim has a gash on his leg, but I think he'll be all right once he sees a doctor. Red Johnny was driving them to the prom. His car is gone." He paused to listen. "OK." He then turned to them.

"First thing we're going to do is take Tim to the hospital. Then I'll take Jean home."

"I want to go home with Jean," Mr. Black said. "Is there any news from the others?"

"No fatalities that we know of," said the driver. "The storm took the roof off the gym but the dance hadn't started yet. The only people there were the band members. They were rehearsing and took shelter in the basement. The oil crews were sent to shelter in time and once the men checked with their families, they helped with the search and rescue team."

Jean was shaking and biting her lip to keep from crying. Tim was not saying anything, but every so often, he would wince. Mr. Black was sitting between them with an arm around each of them. When they had dropped Tim off at the hospital, where his parents were waiting, they continued on to Jean's.

When they arrived at the trailer park (which had mercifully escaped damage), the driver honked in front of Jean's trailer. The door flew open and her

Mom and Dad ran out. Jean threw herself at her mother.

"Oh, Mom, look what happened to my beautiful dress!"

Her Dad wrapped his arms around both of them. "You're beautiful, and you're alive, sweetheart."

He turned to Mr. Black. "John, I knew I could trust you with my little girl." He let go of Jean long enough to pat Mr. Black's shoulder, and continued. "I heard you lost your Cadillac and I know it was your pride and joy. I'm sorry, John, but I'm eternally grateful."

Jean's mother noticed that Jean was shaking and said, "While we were waiting for news, I kept chopping things up to keep busy, so I made a big pot of soup. You all are welcome to come in and have some with us. You, too," she said to the rescue driver.

"Thank you," he said. "We've got a long night ahead, and I haven't had time to eat."

All of the rest of them crowded around the small table. "By the way," the driver said, and he turned to Henry. "Since you lost your car, I can swing by on my way back to headquarters and drop you off at your home. I'm Charles Lindquist." He offered his hand to Mr. Black who took it, saying, "John Black."

A Thatched Cottage

By Virginia Braxton
Submitted on March, 2020

"I don't know anyone in England," Sally thought, as she slit open the envelope with a London address. She found inside a letter purporting to be from a lawyer named J. Carrington, Esq. telling her that she had inherited a property in Kent, England, and would she please contact him immediately.

Sally was congenitally suspicious of anyone pressuring her to share personal information immediately. As far as she was concerned it was the sign of a scam. After a moment's thought she scrawled on the envelope, "Jake, see what the scammers are up to now!"

She enclosed it in a larger envelope, which she addressed to her step-cousin Jake, a lawyer. Jake had come into the family when Sally's Aunt Mildred had married a widower with three children. Jake had a great sense of humor, and it would be fun to see how he would respond. The two of them were pretty much the same age and usually had hung out together at the big family gatherings, watching TV or playing Monopoly.

She had almost forgotten the letter when Jake phoned her one day. "Hello coz, it's Jake. I need to talk to you about that letter from J. Carrington. Can you come to my office, or would you rather meet me for a drink so we can catch up on all the family news as well?"

Sally readily agreed that the latter was preferable, so two days later she and Jake met at a bar near his office in downtown Boston.

"Hello Jake," she said. "Don't keep me in suspense. What's this about John Carrington, Esq.? I am convinced it was a scam."

"Well," Jake responded, "I was suspicious, too, but on the surface he seemed legitimate, so I had our London office check him out. Carrington actually is a respected London lawyer with an Estate and Trust practice."

"Interesting," said Sally, "But I have no contacts or relatives in England."

"That's what you thought," said Jake. "Remember the Thanksgiving when most of us spit into tubes and sent our DNA off to one of those genealogy tracking sites? Well, Carrington's client found you on that site. According to him, his client was your grandfather."

"Good, lord!" said Sally. Between swallows of a restorative drink Sally mused, "Grandma hardly ever mentioned her life in England, but I always knew that

Grandpops wasn't Dad's biological father, because he adopted Dad after he and Grandma married.

"As I understood it, Grandma had been a servant in the big house when Dad's biological father was killed in a farming accident. That's when she came to this country and Dad was born here shortly after she arrived. She didn't talk much, but I think she had a couple of very difficult years as a single mother until she met Grandpops."

"What do you think happened?" Jake asked.

After a pause, Sally said, "It looks as though a man, probably in the big house, got Grandma pregnant and shipped her off here to get her and her child out of the way. I'll bet if she had been alive that Thanksgiving when we did the DNA tests, she would have been very much against them."

"There's more, Sally," said Jake. "You have inherited a cottage on the land. Here's a picture of it."

Sally studied the photo of a thatch roofed cottage, complete with a stone fence and hollyhocks in front of it.

"It's almost too cute to be real, like a Hallmark Card, or a Thomas Kincaid painting! I wonder what the plumbing is like inside."

Jake responded, "Here's the layout Carrington sent of the cottage. You can see that its basically two large rooms on the ground floor, one of which is the family room and kitchen. I think the bathroom must have been added after the cottage was built. See, it's this bump on the back behind the kitchen. There's a piece of land around it, too. Carrington also said he's received a good offer for the property and asks for instructions."

Sally said, "I just don't know. It's so much to take in, and you know how I hate being rushed into a decision!"

"Yeah," Jake said, "Playing Monopoly with you was like playing chess with the Masters. We should have set time limits on you. Take some time to think it over. I'll call you on Thursday, anyway, but in the meantime if you have any questions, you can call me."

When they met a few days later, Sally said, "I don't think I want the cottage, but I want to see what I'm giving up. I can catch a flight from Boston to Heathrow and then go and see the cottage for myself. I haven't taken any vacation since my parents were killed in the accident, so I have plenty of spare time."

"When are you planning to go?" said Jake. "I can certainly ask our London office to help you, if you need it. Better yet, I might get my office to send me there on business."

"I'd like that," said Sally.

* * *

Two weeks later they deplaned at Heathrow, and the next morning they kept their appointment at Mr. Carrington's office.

Mr. Carrington gave them more pictures of the cottage, the keys to it, the floor plan, and directions for reaching it. He explained that by a historical anomaly, Sally's cottage was not part of the entailed land that went with the manor house, so Sally's grandfather was free to will it to her.

Nevertheless, it was surrounded by land which now belonged to Rupert Claxton, who was her grandfather's heir and Sally's biological first cousin, once removed. Carrington suggested that they would probably be more comfortable staying in a hotel in a nearby town rather than in the cottage, and he recommended one for them.

Afterwards, as they were debriefing, Sally said, "I'm almost too tired to think, but there's something here that makes me feel uneasy."

"I agree," Jake responded. "I'm going to check in at our office. Why don't you take a nap while I'm doing that, and we'll catch up at dinner?"

* * *

"Well, did I ever get an earful!" Jake reported to Sally. "No wonder Carrington advised us not to stay in the cottage. There's local controversy about your land. It seems that it is in the middle of a big development Claxton wants to make, so he needs your land. Furthermore, the plan is for upscale housing to be built, while the locals all want more modest housing instead."

"It sounds confused," commented Sally. "Tomorrow, let's go see for ourselves."

* * *

The next afternoon they went to the cottage where Sally used her key, which worked smoothly in the lock. She and Jake found themselves in a room with a huge fireplace, a sink, and a stove. The bathroom was a little room added onto the back.

They had just turned to explore the second room, when a man came through the door without knocking.

"What are you doing in here? You damned bird lovers! I'm calling the police!" he roared.

Sally stiffened. "Please do," she said. "Who are you and what are YOU doing in here?"

"I'm Rupert Claxton," said the man, "I own the manor and all the land around here."

"No," said Sally. "You own most of the land around here. I own this cottage and its land. This is my lawyer, Jacob Detweiler."

Jake smiled, and said, "Yes, here is a card with the address of our London office, and this is my own with my Boston address and mobile number. I'll add Ms. Fenwick's number to it," he said, scribbling Sally's address on the back of his card.

Controlling himself with an effort, Claxton said, "So you're the…"and he quickly changed topics. He then inquired, "Did Carrington convey my offer to you? It's really quite high. The offer is good, and please remember that the cottage is old, and that thatched roofs have a lot of problems. They're not very sanitary, with all sorts of creatures, mice, spiders, etc. living in them, not to mention that the thatch is a fertile place for mold to grow. Also, the pump for the well needs replacing and the water hasn't been tested in years. I'm afraid the old man left you with a white elephant."

"An elephant wouldn't fit in here," said Sally. "It's more like a white rabbit."

Jake muttered something about it disappearing down a hole under his breath, and then more audibly said, "Mr. Claxton, obviously Ms. Fenwick wants to become more familiar with her property before she decides to sell it. When she does make a decision, she will inform Mr. Carrington." Having said that, he ushered Claxton out the door, waited for Sally to lock it, and placed her into their car.

"I really do not like Claxton," Sally said. "He certainly wanted me to sell to him, running down the property that way."

"I didn't like his attitude either," said Jake. "There is something going on here that we don't know about. I have to work tomorrow, and I'll ask my colleagues to recommend a good local lawyer who specializes in real estate. For one thing, I'd like to see a survey of your property and have an independent appraisal of it."

After breakfast the next day, Sally decided she would spend the day walking around the new neighborhood. She stopped at the hotel newsstand and asked for a map of the area.

"All I have is this one of the major roadways in England. GPS really saturates this area, and people depend mostly on it," said the salesperson.

Sally looked at it. "If it's all you have, I'll take it, but I really was hoping for something more detailed; for example, a larger scale map of this area."

"You might try the bookstore. Sometimes they have specialty items, like a walking guide. I see you're dressed for hiking. It's down the block on the right hand side."

Sally found the bookstore, which had several nature books in the window, and entered it hopefully. A very attractive man stood up from behind the counter. Sally realized her mouth was hanging open, so she closed it and said, "Hello. I'm visiting the area and I thought I would do some walking, but I need something more detailed and visual than GPS gives me. Also, if you have one showing nature trails in the area I'd like that one too."

"Yes, we have several which might be suitable," he replied, smiling at her. "I'm John Carter, filling in this morning for the owner. In real life I'm a botanist and

I'm doing research on a lovely little marsh in the area."

"That sounds interesting," Sally responded. "I'm not very knowledgeable about plants. I just categorize them as pretty, useful, invasive, or plain green."

John laughed. "I have to go to the marsh this afternoon to collect some data. Would you like to go with me? It's not a bad walk, and I see you have proper boots on."

Sally hesitated. She knew nothing at all about this man. Catching her hesitation, John said, "Think it over. If you decide to come with me, you can just meet me here at 2:30 pm. Would you like me to mark your route on your map? Actually, the path is well marked, and you don't really need the map, but it helps to visualize the country side."

"I'll think about your invitation," Sally said, and thanked him for all the information.

Back at the hotel, Sally studied the maps while having a cup of coffee. The map which John had marked was highly detailed, and at this scale the marsh looked big. She tried to locate the hotel and her cottage on the map, but concluded that the map was the wrong scale to show them. She decided to go with John, after leaving a note on her dresser telling Jake where she had gone and with whom.

"I'm so glad you decided to come," said John, smiling broadly when she entered the bookstore. He made sure they had supplies and they then started off.

As they walked, they talked. John asked Sally about what she did for a living, and listened, while interrupting to comment on every bird he saw.

Sally said, "I'm a researcher, too. I'm attached to a project at Massachusetts General in health research. Instead of relying on the scientist's trained intuition to come up with a hypothesis to be explored, we mine the mega data to see what hints or trends we can find there. Then we formulate a hypothesis and test it. It's as though we start with the big picture and then narrow it down instead of the other way around."

"It sounds very abstract," responded John. "Do you enjoy it?"

"It is abstract," said Sally. "I spend most of my time with computers one way or another, so I hike for a break. I must admit, however, that your identification of all the birds went right by me without penetrating. It was overwhelming."

"Warning taken," said John. "From now on, I'll forget the birds and only point out a few very special plants."

By now they had passed the big boulder which marked the beginning of the nature walk, and were walking along the edge of the marsh. Sally could tell that the vegetation had changed and instead of talking, John was concentrating on the surroundings.

When they reached a rough bench, John said, "See, over there, those very small orchid-colored flowers? My monitors are those stakes around them. Why don't you sit here, while I record the readings?"

Sally was enjoying the peace and quiet when, to her surprise, her phone rang. She answered it promptly, a little annoyed by the distraction.

"Ms. Fenwick, Rupert Claxton here. Have you decided yet about my offer? It really is generous, considering the run down state of the cottage."

"No, Mr. Claxton, I have not decided yet. I told you I would inform Mr. Carrington when and what I have decided."

John looked up alertly from his notebook as Sally continued. "More money? No, not necessarily. When, and if I make up my mind to sell, I'll inform Mr. Carrington of my asking price. Until then, there is no point in you calling me. I'm going to disconnect now. Goodbye."

Sally disconnected and turned to John. "He really is the most obnoxious man! He keeps pestering me to sell him my cottage right away."

John said, "You must be the American heiress who inherited the Bigelow cottage."

"Well, I'm not exactly an heiress, but I did just inherit a cottage. This is a snapshot of it," Holding out her phone to John.

"Sally," said John. "Meeting you is an unbelievable piece of luck! I'm a member of the local nature conservancy, and we're fighting to have this marsh preserved. It's part of the land that goes with your cottage and Claxton wants to pave it all over entirely. Would you be able to meet with us this evening so we can show you what's at stake and give you the details?"

"Yes," said Sally, "Provided I can bring Jake. He's my lawyer, and we're travelling together. He's in London today."

"Of course," said John, less enthusiastically. "I'll try to arrange the meeting for 8:30 pm. Let's exchange phone numbers, so I can confirm the details with you after I contact the others. You have my number now, if you need it."

Jake's train was late, so Sally barely had time to summarize the events of her day before they hurried off to the pub where the meeting was going to be held. They found four people in a room set up for a PowerPoint presentation.

When one of them, an older man, introduced himself as George Thrasher, Jake responded. "You must be the real estate lawyer?"

"Yes," replied Thrasher.

"What a coincidence," Jake said. "You were recommended to me just this afternoon as the person Sally should have to advise her and to handle the matter of her inheritance. We'll have to confer tomorrow."

"I'm not exactly a neutral party," said Thrasher. "I'm committed to the work of the nature conservancy, but if there's a conflict of interest, I'll recommend someone else. Let's get started on the presentation so you know what Claxton's proposal is, what the stakes are, and how we locals and members of the conservancy feel about it."

The first slide was a map showing the Claxton property, and right in the middle, in a contrasting color, was Sally's property. The second slide was a picture of the development model Claxton had presented to the county council.

Neither Sally's property, nor the marsh, appeared where Sally thought they should be. The third frame was an overlay, outlining Sally's property, including the marsh on top of a picture of the model.

Sally's property was in the middle of the development. John Carter went on at length about the rare plant which Sally had seen that afternoon, and at even greater length about the rare bird which had been sighted in the same area. Sally mentally dubbed the bird as a "tit-willow."

By the time the meeting broke up, George Thrasher had promised to give Sally and Jake a copy of the survey of Sally's land done for the nature conservancy and to engage an appraiser on Sally's behalf.

Sally was glad that she and Jake had agreed to meet for brunch so they could sleep in the next day. She was particularly annoyed when her phone rang early and she identified Claxton's number. She let it go to voice mail. When she listened to his message, he was once more pressuring her to sell. At last he said goodbye and thought he broke the connection, but Sally heard him mutter "Dim witted cow!" before the connection was cut.

In the days while Sally was waiting for the appraisal of the property, she seemed to spend the afternoons with John Carter and the evenings with Jake, hashing things out. Jake reminded her that she was going over the same ground over and over. He also wondered to himself what influence Carter was having on her.

Finally Sally received the appraisal. The property was worth four times what Claxton had offered her. "That settles, it!" she exclaimed, "There's no way I would let him have it! Jake, it's time to tell Mr. Carrington that I will not sell to Claxton."

"But, Sally," queried Jake, "What are you going to do with it? Have you decided to move here and live in it?"

"No way," Sally replied.

"Then what are you going to do with it?"

"What I'd really like to do is give it to the nature conservancy. The group here is part of a national organization that not only has nonprofit status, but also one of the royals is its patron—maybe even Prince Charles. I could deed it to them and give them a donation toward the repair of the cottage. Then they could rent the cottage and have a source of income for the conservancy. I'm sure Mr. Thrasher could set that up for us."

"I like that idea," said Jake. "I'll see if Thrasher can meet with us Saturday morning." Privately he thought he'd never seen Sally make a decision that fast.

"Do you want me to let Carrington know that you are not accepting the Claxton offer?"

"Let's wait until it is all done and irrevocable," Sally said with a gleam in her eye. "Then we'll hit him with a fait de accompli."

"As you probably noticed," she said changing the subject, "I haven't done anything about researching Grandma. When we were going through her things after she died, I found her old passport from when she emigrated, and other documents concerning her application for U.S. citizenship. I brought them with me and they furnish a good starting place. I know she came from this village, and since she was a staunch Episcopalian in the U.S. I assume she was a Church of England member here. I made an appointment for tomorrow afternoon with the local pastor so we can search the church records."

Jake was in high spirits when he and Sally met the next evening. He announced that Mr. Thrasher would be delighted to meet with them Saturday, but he noticed that Sally was subdued.

"How did things go with the pastor?" he queried.

"It seems as though what we suspected is true," reported Sally. "Gran's surname when she emigrated was Waller, and we found her baptismal record with the name "Edith Waller," but found no marriage record. She was in the States and had had Dad by the time she turned 19! The people here, meaning the Claxton's, just treated her as though she were disposable! It makes me so mad!"

"Oh, and dear Rupert tried again to call me, but I didn't answer. Did he try to call you?"

"Not so far as I know," answered Jake.

"The pastor said that while many of the old gentry's class have adjusted to current times, the Claxton's keep walking around as though it were still the 1700s. They're not very well liked as a result."

"Oh, and he said that the Wallers were an old family around here, but they've died out. He said there are a lot of them listed in the church graveyard."

"It's still light," said Jake. "We could go look at their tombstones, if you want to."

"No thanks," Sally responded. "I'd rather have a nightcap and turn in early."

* * *

The next day they met Thrasher and told him what Sally's plan was? She admitted that she wanted to frustrate Rupert Claxton by giving her land to the conservancy. She also told Thrasher what they believed had happened to her grandmother and the role they surmised the Claxton's had played. She wanted her gift named, "The Edith Waller Nature Walk."

Sally said she was quite prepared to give up the cottage and would make a donation of it so it could be modernized and then rented out to provide income for the conservancy.

"I have an idea," said Thrasher. "Currently the conservancy is renting a storefront in Tonbridge as our county headquarters. We could move our headquarters to the cottage and put up a large, but tasteful, sign saying, *The Edith Waller Nature Walk*, sponsored by the nature conservancy. Claxton could not enter his gate without seeing it."

"Excellent!" exclaimed Sally.

"Is there any way he can stop you?" asked Jake. "Are there any liens or obscure regulations he could use to get an injunction blocking your plan?"

"No," said Thrasher. "We in the conversancy researched it exhaustively when we were trying to find a way to stop the development. Besides, the county board and the judiciary here are not under the thumb of the Claxton's."

"I'll get to work on the documents right away. I should have the essential ones ready by Monday evening, and the rest can be handled long distance. By the way, how much longer are you going to be here?"

"I have to be at work in Boston on Thursday. How about you, Sally? Do you want to do some more sightseeing?"

"No, I'm ready to leave as soon as we get the papers signed."

Mr. Thrasher was as good as his word. The essential papers were completed by Monday afternoon, and written notice refusing Claxton's offer was sent to Carrington.

That evening the conservationists, including John Carter, had gathered in the pub to fete Sally and Jake, when Rupert Claxton called. This time Sally answered the phone. "Why, yes, Mr. Claxton," Sally cooed, "We just sent Mr. Carrington our official notification."

"It's about time!" Claxton interrupted.

"I am deeding the cottage and the land to the nature conservancy for a preserve to be named in honor of my grandmother, Edith Waller." She held the phone away from her ear while Claxton fulminated and the crowd cheered. Still cooing sweetly she said, "I'm going to disconnect now. Goodbye."

Tuesday evening, while they were in the holding area waiting to board the plane, Jake said, "Sally, I know you hate to be rushed, but it's high time you started thinking about me."

"Why you?"

"Yes, me. You and me. Us. I want to marry you. I want you to be my wife, for us to have children, and a life together. Start thinking about it, now, and try not to take more than a year to decide."

Sally looked at Jake. It just felt so . . . right, being with him. "Yes, but ?"

"But?"

"But I want to be wooed, to be courted."

Jake grabbed her and kissed her thoroughly. When they paused, he said, "That's only a sample. There's more where that came from."

"Good," said Sally, as boarding was announced. "I wonder how Aunt Mildred will react." They both laughed and, still laughing, they boarded the plane.

Santa Reflects

By Virginia Braxton
Submitted on April, 2020

When he saw a puffed up, blown up, lit up 10-foot snowman on the grass between two real palm trees south of Napa, California, Santa felt his spirits sag and knew he needed a break. What did that snowman have to do with his ancestral Bishop Nicholas who suffered in Roman jails and brought back to life three little pickled boys?

Fat chance to neither show his own disgust, with lumps of coal in this green clean place where people would not even know what coal was nor what lumps of it signified.

He himself was full of milk and cookies, but his team still needed hay and nowadays there was none of that to put out. Circling the town, he spotted a pond in a fenced and grassy park. Landing there he unhitched his team to graze and rest while he walked around the town.

No one paid attention to him. He was just another fat man with whiskers in a red suit. He thought sarcastically, "We ought to have a union," and was startled to see three ersatz Santa's with placards picketing outside a store.

Then he saw two more Santa's and followed them. They went into a bar, (fortunately no children were inside), and so he sat where he could hear them talk. One complained. "They pulled my beard to see if it was real, but the glue held fast." The other said, "This kid was sitting on my lap and had an accident which stained my trousers, and made it look as though the accident was mine!" Santa buried his head in his hands. He felt an arm around his shoulders. "Hey, fellow sufferer, join us for a martini!"

"Can't," said Santa, "I'm driving, so it's coffee only," and he left through the nearest door only to find himself in the biggest mall he had ever seen. It smelled of popcorn and garlic, and was filled with people who seemed harried and tense. He wanted fresh air so he found another exit.

Outside he encountered an enormous hot air balloon of Rudolph, whose nose blinked red each time Rudolph swayed in the breeze. Probably motion activated, thought Santa, but that creature couldn't pull a sleigh—no musculature! It really was an insult to his team. Slyly, carefully, he undid some of the tethers which grounded this Rudolph and trudged on.

Then he saw a group of people who weren't shopping. They were heading away from the mall, and they talked to each other and laughed. Some of them were carrying bundles. He fell in behind them, trying to hear what they were saying. He caught the word "Bethlehem" and thought that sounded hopeful, so he moved closer. Then just as he heard, "Nativity," they stopped suddenly and he bumped into one of the men.

That man turned to him and said, "Hey Santa, we're going to the Christ Kindle Market to help some friends put on a flash Nativity. Why don't you join us?"

Santa demurred, "A Nativity's not very flashy. I'm not sure—."

"Oh, all the flash means is that people in a public space suddenly start performing. They can sing, dance, play instruments, all kinds of things, but it just happens with no warning. We're tired of the commercialism around Christmas so we and our friends are going to do a flash Nativity. Why don't you come with us?"

"But," protested Santa, "St. Nicholas wasn't at the Nativity. He didn't come along until almost three hundred years later."

"True," said the man. "But, look. All you would have to do is to take off your red hat, and throw a shepherd's robe over yourself and you'd fit in beautifully. I have an extra robe here."

"All right," said Santa taking the proffered robe and putting his hat into his pocket. He walked with the group and stood among them when they greeted their friends. They shuffled around putting on their makeshift costumes. There were men draped as angels, and there were travel-worn Magi. There was a holy family with a baby in a car seat. There were musicians.

Then the musicians played a fanfare, and the whole group stepped out of the crowd and stood together. The musicians kept playing while the shepherds stood around, the angels waved their wings, and the Magi bowed to the Babe. Mary held her baby high. He looked straight at the shepherd-Santa and grinned and waved at him. Santa beamed. The musicians played "In Dulce Jabillo," and it was over.

"Thank you," said Santa, as he handed back the shepherd's robe. "That was great! Now I have to get back to work."

He put on his hat and left to get his team. As he drew near the place he'd left his reindeer, he saw that the Rudolph balloon had drifted free and his nose was illuminating a noisy and chaotic scene.

There were police cars, and a large van labelled "Animal Control Department." Men wearing heavy clothing and wielding ominous looking tranquilizer guns were clustered at the gate to the park. They were surrounded by dozens of three and four year olds clinging to their legs and howling, while their parents tried to pull them away. Among the children's cries, Santa could distinguish a few words such as, "No! Santa! No! Rudolph! Bambi!"

As an ACD worker raised his gun, a mother flung herself at him crying "My baby, my baby!" In the melee the ACD worker misfired and the darts hit Rudolph, who deflated with a whoosh, blanketing most of the crowd. Santa ran around the heaving carcass and began to harness his team. The people who were not under Rudolph began chanting, "Go Santa, go! Go Santa, go!"

Liftoff was greeted with jubilant cheers. Santa waved as he gave the traditional farewell, "Merry Christmas to all, and to all a good night!"

Honor among Thieves

By Virginia Braxton
Submitted on March, 2020

Dwayne said, "Thank you, ma'am, for riding with me," and then, as soon as the woman was safely deposited, he gunned the motor to get away. Stupid snowbird! Complaining about the heat! What did she expect in the Arizona desert in the summertime? And moaning about having to sell their house here because they no longer could afford two houses!

His own house was an adobe survival near a dry creek that he'd won in a crap game, and he'd made sure that the titles for the house, land, and mineral rights, were properly transferred to himself. Fortunately, an earlier owner had installed indoor plumbing and the electricity that he really needed to run his computer. Even in this heat the thick walls made the place relatively cool, so he didn't have to use the swamp cooler, but dirt from the adobe ceiling drifted down all the time. He'd protected his computer with a cage, but maybe he'd sleep better if he did what the old timers had done and installed a canopy near the ceiling to catch the flaking dirt as it fell.

Oh, well. The house was useful now, and driving for Lyft put food on the table, but once he'd made his big score, he was going to have a mansion with proper air conditioning, a swimming pool, and a butler.

His cell phone dinged, and he saw he had a pickup, not too far from his own place, at one of the super luxurious resorts—two people heading for downtown. He sized up the two men as they got into his car. Not from around here, and over dressed for the heat in business suits and ties—a bit flashy. He decided to let them talk to each other and drove slowly, while he listened very carefully.

Dwayne had no trouble hearing, but it was mostly, Lenny this, what would Bruce do, and a lot of real estate talk. Still there was something that sounded as though they were running a con. Dwayne wondered why they would go to all that trouble, when the internet offered a million easier ways to make a pile. He dropped them at a downtown office building and went about his day.

He had barely finished breakfast the next day, when his phone dinged—another pickup at the resort. It was the same men, still in suits, but now without neckties. They recognized him.

"Say, aren't you the same driver we had yesterday? Do you have a lock on this territory, or something?"

"Not really, but I live out this way and hardly any other driver does. Mostly I have to drive into town to get fares."

"Oh, have you been here long?"

"All my life."

The taller man said casually, "Colorful country. A fellow in the bar last night said something about gold in the rocks around here."

Dwayne perked up. Was this bait intended for him, or could he play them with it? "There's a story about a high grade mine in those mountains over there, but its location has been lost. Before we had GPS, every summer someone would die in the desert looking for it. And a lot of the canyons still don't have GPS."

"So there really is gold around here?" the tall man asked.

"Sure, there's a lot of gold around here, but it's mostly low grade" Dwayne replied.

"Could it be mined?"

"Sure, but mining it would take a lot of water, and water's the one thing around here that's more precious than gold," Dwayne responded. Then he told himself to shut up and just listened for the rest of the ride.

As they came to their destination, the other man said, "Why don't you give us your information, so we can put you down as our favorite driver? Then instead of just driving to town in the mornings, you'd have a fare."

"Sure," said Dwayne giving him his company ID. "Much obliged," he said as he thought, "Yes!"

For the next several days, every morning Dwayne's phone dinged for him to pick up the two men. Bob was a distinguished looking older man and seemed to be the leader. Lee was younger and did not seem too bright, but Dwayne wondered if he was just acting.

One morning Bob said, "Does it ever rain around here?"

"Sure, in the summer. And it's solid."

"What do you mean solid?"

"It's like a whole swimming pool coming down on your head at once, with no drops, just water."

Bob nodded. "Bet people get pretty excited."

"They sure do."

Bob turned to Leo and continued talking, complaining because they could not reach Bruce, who had to give final approval for their deal. But Dwayne noticed that, as usual, Bob ended up talking about gold, the prospects for striking it, and the need for water to process it.

One day, as if by accident, Dwayne let slip that he owned land in the area. Bob's eyes gleamed, "Could we look for gold on your land?"

"Maybe, but you've got to sign papers. That's the way it's done," said Dwayne.

"Regular little businessman, aren't you," commented Bob.

As he made an affirmative grunt, Dwayne thought, "Hell, yes! I've got a Master's in business administration."

Two days later they met downtown in the afternoon when Dwayne's fares were slow. Bob and Leo signed the papers Dwayne had drawn up allowing them prospecting rights on his land for a limited time, and they paid Dwayne with a cashier's check as he had specified.

The plan was to construct a flume in the wash directing the flow, (when it came), into a narrow channel through Dwayne's land between the creek and the bank where his house was. Dwayne thought messing with the creek bed was probably illegal, but he didn't mention it to Bob and Leo. He also persuaded them to buy a generator to power floodlights so they could work at night when it was cooler.

They went to work. Bob and Leo abandoned their business suits and, to Dwayne's surprise, began doing heavy labor. He suggested that they could hire someone to do the worst of it, but Bob and Leo were adamant that no one else be involved. Leo told Dwayne, confidentially, that they were waiting for someone who was on an extended vacation to authorize their proposal and that in the meantime they were going to keep busy prospecting for gold. They were also moving to less expensive lodgings.

"Makes sense," Dwayne replied. He wondered if their deal had fallen through.

The night came when they were almost done. They only had to fill in a small part of the flume on Dwayne's side of the gulley. Then Leo, straightening up, said, "What's that noise? Sounds like thunder, but there're no clouds."

"Get out!" yelled Dwayne, recognizing the sound of a gully washer. "Get out!" He scrambled up the bank pulling the men with him just as the water came roaring down.

Thundering like an avalanche, the muddy water tossed debris ahead of itself. It wedged two logs the size of telephone poles against the edge of the flume, directing the water though the unfinished side against the bank where Dwayne's house stood. Dwayne saw the edge of the bank begin to crumble and retreated. He kept retreating until he was on the far side of his house as the force of the water took away more and more of the bank. Then he saw his house quiver and fall into the torrent. It dissolved—just mud.

The three men looked silently down at the water which could have killed them. To venture in now would be suicidal.

Leo patted Dwayne's shoulder. "That's tough to look at. Come on, let's go to the tavern. I'll buy you dinner."

But it was Bob who, after a few beers, turned the conversation to their project. "Dwayne," he said, "How long do you think it will be before the water is gone?"

"Depends. Might be almost gone in the morning, or it might be a couple of days. Depends on how much water was in the mountains. Of course, the water brings down a lot of gravel and sand as well as the mud and debris."

"Could it have brought down gold?"

"It's possible."

Bob hesitated a moment before saying, "Why don't we meet by the generator (which was upstream of where Dwayne's house had been) tomorrow night, and see what it looks like?"

"OK. Right now I have to check into a motel, and tomorrow I'll be getting organized. Better get some waders to wear in case we can go down into the stream bed."

Dwayne knew that even if they did find his computer, the mud and sand would have destroyed it, but unbeknownst to Bob and Leo, he already had the money to replace it. Furthermore he had been faithful about backing up and storing the backup off site, so his work building connections on the dark web would not be lost. He even had insurance on the house, but he wasn't sure it would be smart to bring in an insurance adjuster.

The next night they met and Dwayne led the way into the muck. After several hours of back breaking searching, they found Dwayne's coffee maker, the remains of his computer, and a number of small rocks. When they washed the rocks in the motel bathtub, only a few of them glittered, and those were just "fools' gold."

Bob and Leo sat silently eating their take out Chinese, visibly dejected. Dwayne thought, this is the moment.

"Look," he said, "there are easier ways to make money than panning for fool's gold. If I had a computer, we could get rich fast."

"Tell us about it," said Bob. "I'm not up on all this technology."

Dwayne began, "A lot of people who use the internet are very trusting, and we can use that to make easy money. Here's what we do...."

Kent Humpal Stories

House About That

By Kent Humpal
Submitted on December, 2019

The dire and gloomy weather reports and predictions had started a week earlier, so everyone should be prepared to expect the worst. This part of Kansas was in Tornado Alley. The tornadoes came up from Oklahoma and blasted into Kansas. A few towns were small and isolated and protected by their geographical locations, but individual farms often got ripped apart.

Dorothy Gale Bolger kept an eye on the sky and her ear to the radio. The last really big tornado was in 1939 when her Great Grandma was a young girl, and now she was in her 90th year.

Dorothy pulled into the cinder block garage and scurried into the house through the kitchen door. As she turned on the TV, Toto number 6 or 7, she wasn't sure, popped through the dog door to greet her enthusiastically, whirling and prancing around her legs.

Grabbing a snack and a bottle of water from the refrigerator, she turned on the TV. The TV people were all screaming as they ran for shelters. A piercing whistle was sounding from the TV, as a band on the bottom of the screen issued an evacuation warning, or which found another shelter-in-place.

The house looked like the old place, but it had been upgraded and reinforced over the years. A complete basement was added for one thing, but also a safe room had been built next to the basement.

"Oh! Crap!" thought Dorothy. "Here, Toto, let's go to the safe room, for its closer to us."

Shutting the door behind her, setting the lock and arming it with her fingerprints, she settled down in a recliner with Toto snuggling in beside her. She looked around the stark room with no windows open, and to the other doors and windows that were sealed with water-proof gaskets. Ventilation was filtered, while concealed cameras fed a small monitor on the wall, and a small battery backed up the monitor and refrigerator power.

Abruptly everything shut down. "Well, so much for the backup power," she said to Toto. But surprisingly, the monitor feed kept going. Sitting in total darkness, except for the small monitor screen, her thoughts drifted to the family stories—fairy tales, she always had thought.

She was all alone. Her parents had taken Great Grandma to LA for the 80th anniversary of the movie made of her supposed exploits. There were only a few aged Munchkins and stand-ins left from the original cast. Grandma had outlived the principal actors and was now the main attraction.

Sitting alone she began to rethink Great Grandma's stories. Malarkeys, the Family, and Frank Baum fit Great Grandma into his fantasy. There was no Oz, no Wizard, no Wicked Witches, but rather it was all a tale to take the people's mind off the Great Depression and the War in Europe.

Dorothy dozed off only to wake up a few hours later when Toto nudged her and gave her a soft bark. The monitor camera showed clear skies. The class-five or higher tornado was gone, but so was the familiar landscape on the monitor.

Dorothy pressed her thumb to the screen and the lower part clicked open. She opened the door and gazed out on a Technicolor World, containing a bright sky, a brilliantly colored landscape of large flowers, ultra-green grass, and trees with bark faces and undulating limbs.

"Where are we, Toto?" she asked with a quivering voice. The house and farm were nowhere to be seen. The safe-room was by itself on a quaint village street. Daring to open the door and step out, she muttered to herself. "Holy Schise, God damn it Toto, Great Grandma didn't make it all up. I think we are actually in the Land of Oz!"

The rooms were all at an add angle, so she stepped away and looked down. OMG!! They had landed on someone. She looked at the skinny legs in striped stockings sticking out from under the room. "Yep, just like Great Grandma had described it."

Toto gave a disdainful sniff and lifted his leg over the still limbs. She sizzled a little as the dog's urine touched them. She then became aware that a crowd was gathering around her. Toto barked at a couple of vertically challenged people pulling on his ears and tail.

"Who are you," spoke Dorothy. "What do you want? Where are you? Where am I? You are a Munchkin, aren't you?"

Two spokesmen in broadly striped garish suits stepped forward and one handed her a card. "I'm Marvin Munchkin, the 3rd, and my colleague is Maxwell Munchkin. We represent the Cannibal Vaping Guild."

Before she could introduce herself, a van pulled up. It had an iridescent psychedelic rainbow on its side labeled Fairies, Goblins, Troll Elves, Leprechauns, Ogres, and Banshees.

A wild-haired indescribable person leaped out yelling, "Don't sign up with them. Our agency represents the diverse clientele of Oz."

Before she could reply, two gaudily striped Emerald and Gold squad cars arrived. "Hold it; hold it, you in the funny blue suit. Call off that wild beast and please surrender."

Dorothy, beginning to rally herself, replied, "Surrender to whom and for what? I'm a refugee from a natural disaster."

As the arguing continued among the various groups, a thin individual in a denim business suit, straw protruding from his wrists, stepped forward.

"Can I help you, young woman? You seem bewildered, yet familiar. Your name doesn't happen to be Dorothy, does it?"

"Why yes, how did you know?

"Our firm has a portrait from years ago hanging in our Office. The original partners had it painted. It looks just like you, but with different clothing of course. Our firm's motto is: *Brains, Heart, and Courage at the Click of your Heels.*"

"Young woman, come along with us. We're taking you to Emerald City to appear before the Wizard," yelled the Keystone-styled policeman.

"What's your authority, spoke the serious faced straw attorney. We are the Immigration Agency of Oz, and this woman crossed our borders in a universal unauthorized room, while crushing a citizen of Oz. Citing a 1939 ordinance, we must take her into our custody."

Thrusting her into a zebra-corn pulled wagon they set off on a tarnished brass colored road to the Emerald City. Dorothy looked at her surroundings as they whisked through a forest, then a poppy field, and finally came to the City of Emerald Gates.

Being wide open they soon arrived at the City Hall. Surrounded by citizens and creatures of all kinds and colors, Dorothy was escorted into an overly decorated and elaborate waiting room. A tin man appeared through a side door.

"I got here as soon as I heard the news. We drew straws in the office to see who would represent you, and I won," the Tin Man said.

She could hear his heart rhythmically beating in his hollow chest. A trio of charming, but shy young lions, came in with one saying, "We're here to protect you."

Then they sauntered off to form up with their pride. Their eyes kept roving to various spots, where Flying Monkeys drifted through the hallways.

Then the curtains opened. Seated on a throne was an over-weight, red-faced man, wearing a wizard's robe trimmed in Gold. On his head, barely covering a swoop of orange hair over-hanging his brow was a wizard's hat with a short bill. Embroiled in gold thread were the letters MOGA.

"I am the greatest wizard of all time. Who are you?"

"I'm Dorothy of Kansas," she replied.

"Why is she here?" he blustered. "I didn't send for her. You stand in front of me and turn in a circle. Not bad. A little thin for my taste, but not bad at all."

"Your wizardness," spoke the head agent. "She entered illegally with her vehicle, a flying room that landed on the Red Witch and crushed her flat. She was your Witch of the Interior, a cabinet member."

"So what, witches are a dime a dozen," he responded.

"But she controlled the union of Flying Monkeys. They'll want citizen's rights and the vote. Besides, her family has a long record in Oz. Her Great Grandmother committed homicide, crushed the wicked witch of the East with a house, and then water- boarded the sister of the Wicked Witch of the West to death in her own castle, thus releasing these damn pestiferous monkeys from bondage. Now she has done the same with the Red Witch, crushed her flat, and stolen her Amber Slippers."

Dorothy looked down, and by gosh they were on her feet. A perfect fit too. "Those are Panel la Gucci's, worth a fortune, your highest Lord Wizard."

"Yes, very costly. What do you have to say for yourself slut, I mean young woman?" He spoke loudly so all could hear.

The Tin Attorney spoke up. "Wizard, on what do you base your authority? The last wizard flew off in gas bags which we found appropriate the same day that Dorothy left OZ. Now you show, 80 years later, claiming to have innervated the wizard ship. Explain how?"

"How dare you. I'll have your license dismissed from office." The words spewed from his reddened face.

"My title says the all-powerful, who are you to dispute that! I need to know, for the record of you being a natural born citizen of OZ," said the woods man as his heart began ringing the hour.

"I'll have you know that I inherited the Ozymandias Hotel, the Great Wizard lodge, and the Golf Course from my Grandfather. I had to cut a few corners to pay it off, I mean settle some debts, but I own them, except for a mortgage or two," responded the wizard.

As he grew more agitated he began to fill with more and more hot air. Reaching his limits to contain it, he began to float. Curiously a couple of the Flying Monkeys nudged him over the courtyard. Caught by a crosswind, he was last seen wriggling his arms and legs, shouting he was within his power as he passed over the Ozzandian Alps.

With a new Parliament made up of the various groups and the newly citizenized monkeys, the Munchkin-led coalition named a Prime Minister. Dorothy's appeal that the safe room was under automated control and she was not its pilot was upheld. The princess of Oz, as the token head of Oz, granted her clemency. Clicking the heels of the amber slippers, she and Toto went home.

The media, catching on to the story plus her Great Grandmas story made her a big star. A major shoe company paid for the right to manufacture the amber shoes. Dorothy and her Grandma appeared on the Late Night show, 60 minutes, and Ellen De Generates. A movie sequel to the Wizard of Oz was set up by Disney Studios. Toto became a spokes dog for a major pet food company. The self- proclaimed Great Wizard apparently came down in the Siberian Tundra, or so the Russian Government claimed. The farm house was rebuilt in the same place.

Recycle of Life

By Kent Humpal
Submitted on November, 2019

Josh was stuck in traffic again. The commute used to start jamming up at 4:15 or 4:30 pm, but now it started jamming up at 2:45 or 3:00 pm. Good thing he telecommuted as much as possible, but he has to appear sometimes, or they forget that he exists—just a name without a face.

Josh remembered his grade school years. He walked or rode his bike everywhere. Use common sense and then obey unwritten natural rules. Now they have laws governing everything, but most laws are seldom obeyed.

He looked in the side mirror—yep right on time—the big truck coming in is on the right. The same truck every day forces himself into the lane, regardless of the traffic. Also up ahead the red Prius was dive bombing into the right-turn lane.

He had begun to recognize faces and vehicles from months ago. It was always the same drivers making the same selfish moves at the same places every day. It wasn't the cycle that upset him. It was the same thing every day, over and over again. It was like the movie <u>Ground Hog Day</u>, except he hadn't found a way to change the pattern. Talk about being in a rut! The trip from Mt. View to San Bruno was getting to be almost automatic for him.

His real life began when he got home to an older house located near the Old Skyline Highway. Four of the homes were connected together, with two nearby homes hooked together looking almost amateur. He managed the house for his grandparents, who lived in Nampa, Idaho, where things were cheaper and much slower.

Anson had a studio and practice area set up in the triple garage behind the house. He and Josh were in a small band together with three other guys. They hoped to start a new band with new material in the future.

They all had jobs in the electronics or communications industries now, which were often merged. Josh's degrees in Sound Engineering and Programming kept him employed, but he really wanted to be in a successful band.

He pulled into the driveway and parked on what was once the lawn. After gulping down left-overs and ice tea he headed into the studio. Anson had made the place as secure as possible. Expensive sound equipment, plus old instruments, made it tempting for burglars.

Having listened to friends that had lost favorite guitars, keyboards, and amps to theft had left them leery. He ran through the current set on his Martin, bought from a neighbor with cash and some labor.

The songs were all Doobie Brothers, Pink Floyd, and Nirvana with a few Grateful Dead mixed in. He doodled around on the Mandolin he found at a Reno pawn shop, where some musician had finally left it behind.

Anson came in and they loaded up their old van. It was not just any van, but a van that had been once owned by a plumber—solid sides, lockable doors—all very hard to break into. The only change had been to add two side windows of thick polystyrene for light to be able to enter.

They headed off to their weekly gig, playing other group's songs for the umpteenth time. Thirty minutes later they pulled into the parking lot off highway one. Party goers and true fans were waiting there for them at Club DejaVue.

Best Wishes or . . .

By Kent Humpal
Submitted on November, 2019

I was a Rat, at least under the Chinese New Year's agenda. The dinner was coming to an end. There were eight of us, family and close friends, without any children at this dinner.

It was Emily that came up with the idea. "Hey, let's put all the fortune cookies on the turn table. That will be more like fate." She then spun the table and took the cookie that came closest to her.

She had given a tentative spin and the table slowly moved around. Russ and Chris took hold and said, "You've got to give it a real spin, Emily. A good thing no dishes were on it, as it swung wildly and rapidly around. A busboy reached for it, but it had slowed down, scattering the folded cookies around the table.

I reached for the one on my left, but the cookie on the right seemed to leap into my hands. It almost gave off a glow. A little brighter than the others, I thought. It must be the lights, or a beam from the mirrored walls striking the cookies surface.

Snap, Crackle, Pop, just like Rice Crispi's. They were being opened all around us. I could hear the fortunes being read—**Prepare for the Future, Good Things Will Be Yours, Good Friends Bearing Good Fortune,** etc.

My cookie seemed to open on its own. The slips of paper were different for my cookies. The others were the usual white with black lettering, whereas this one was Imperial Red with Gold lettering. It read—**Buddha grants you one wish**.

OK, I thought then that it turned in my fingers and another message was on the other side. **Confucian Cautions, be careful what you wish for**. I thought over the two messages and I looked down to read them again and they began to dissolve into ideographic Chinese symbols.

I was going to ask the rest of the party about their fortunes—any red and black disappearing messages? They would laugh and ask if I had had too many beers.

My mind flashed on to all the old myths and fairy tales. Things never turned out the way you wanted, like the "Midas Touch," the "Portrait of Dorian Grey," the "Monkey's Paw," or "Aesop's Fables." Even modern movies showed the opposite side of wishes granted, like the wishes granted in "Big," "Switched," or "Ground Hog Day."

I thought about the universal wishes—no war, no famine, no diseases, no natural disasters, or no eternal life. How could the world support the population and govern itself? If religion ended would morals or good will also end?

Slipping the blank paper into my pocket I turned to the others and said, "Did anyone get a quaint or meaningful message?"

Better to be a Scene

By Kent Humpal
Submitted on November, 2019

Honestly, I try not to listen in on other people's conversations. It's not polite, and I don't want them listening in to mine, especially if I'm talking to family or close friends, but sometimes you can't help it. With all the phones and communication devices around it's almost impossible.

For example, the other night I was at the 24 hour mini market picking up milk, a six pack, and a frozen pizza, and this guy walks by in the paper goods aisle. He's got his cell phone speaker on and is talking to someone. This is what I overheard.

"Yeah, George, I'm in the market now, you know that quickie place off of White and Highway 87. OK, what's the problem? I've got the list in my head—no paper, no it's not on my phone. What? Go into the cleaning products section. Speak up, for I can't hear you well. Yeah, ok, I've got you on the speaker now, on low. Some guy's watching so I'm going to be quiet for a few seconds."

Curiously I passed him, but caught his image on those big convex mirrors. I moved over to where I could hear him, but he couldn't see me. I picked up the voices—you know his and the other speaker. It wasn't a woman—you know a wife, or girlfriend. The voices came in low but were clear. These new speakers are really marvelous.

"He said 2 gallons each of chlorine bleach, any kind, and another 2 gallons of ammonia, and then you get it and go to the all night drug store and buy the same thing there. And then bring everything to the old warehouse where we've been shooting."

I know these two items can be lethal when combined. You get chlorine gas like they use in the war. Also you can do yourself in if you're not careful, especially by the ammonia, if you're in a closed space or if you're over it and breathe in the fumes.

I'm thinking, what are they cleaning up or are they making a bomb of some sort. I dig out my phone when I reach the counter and the clerk is putting the items in a cardboard box for their easier carrying. I am about to call 911, when the clerk speaks up.

"Hey, Ray, are you and Jaime about to wrap up the movie for your film class soon? I heard the old building you are using is being torn down soon also."

"We're filming the last scenes tonight. Halley got off work early and Frank and Miquel are part of the class. We're using hand-held cameras and setting off the explosion and vapors as soon as we clear out. The fire department is going to use it as a training session too."

"That's good Ray. Let me know when you put it on the Internet so I can see your work," the clerk calls out as Ray left. "Good filming."

I put my phone back in my pocket and set my stuff down on the counter. "Walt," the clerk said, "That group has been working on that short film for three months now. They had to get all kinds of papers signed from the city, police, and fire departments, plus State and Federal Bureaus. Luckily the old building was going down anyway to make room for an apartment complex. I Hope they are successful. Here is your total. Have a good night."

I left, more resolved now than ever to ignore phone and personal conversations. But then, what if it had been a plot?

Reflections on Life

By Kent Humpal
Submitted on August, 2020

"Damn it, I fell asleep in front of the TV again. I sat up and groggily started to stand, only to slip back onto the lounge chair. I've got to start going to bed earlier, I thought to myself. My legs were partially asleep from being crossed one over the other, so I again had to stagger when I sat up.

"Hell, I'm getting old," I mumbled, as I finally stood. I might as well go to bed, for its after eleven. My eyes and ears caught the end of the sports cast on the late night news channel. Moving to the kitchen sink, I turned on the cold water tap and filled a glass with water. Finding the remote on the side table I turned off the TV.

Turning to the entry door I caught something moving on the porch. "Who the hell is coming around at this time of night?" I wondered. The image got closer as I stepped forward. It was a man, casually dressed, with slippers, and he raised his hand as I moved to fasten the door.

Somewhat disheveled and grumpy looking I thought that he must be upset about something. I waited for him to ring the bell or knock, but he did neither. White haired, about my size, he looked old. Putting on my glasses, I gave him a closer look. God that is me or at least it's my reflection. I can't be that old! The image died as I turned off the lights. Feeling relieved, but depressed, I wandered off to bed.

Character Development

By Kent Humpal
Submitted on March, 2020

He finished the paragraph and closed down the laptop. It was late, and he'd missed dinner again. Hungry, he went to the fridge and looked over the shelves. A beer looked good, but milk would be better at this hour. Hah, there was some leftover ham and scalloped potatoes. Cold or microwaved, it was better if the spuds were warm, he thought. After he ate the warmed food he went to bed, trying not to disturb his wife or the incumbent cat. He was instantly asleep.

Barry and Chet left on the I-cloud in suspension or seeming suspension, stretched, looked at each other and sighed. Barry spoke up, "Chet, where is he going with this story, he's left us or at least me, in an untenable position."

"I don't know. He never leaves an outline or page of notes, not even marginal ideas. If you think you're bad off, I just left an angry wife and a teen-ager out past curfew on the previous page," replied Chet.

"I hate being left up in the air, finish a scene, at least a voice over or a scene shift."

"What are we anyway? A sit-com, or a crime drama," asked Barry. "I haven't got a clue from the lines I have seen so far."

Chet, usually the comic relief in the show, replied after some thought. "You know, I haven't a clue. You don't think this is a finale do you? I'm just beginning to develop as a character."

"Oh, great, now you put that it my head," replied Barry somberly.

"The last time he was head-writer the network cancelled the show at mid-crisis. Left me hanging in the back of my mind, I was in limbo until he wrote me in as a bit character in an unsold screen play."

Chet settled into the last pose he was given before his creator shut down. Barry went back to leaning on the kitchen counter, looking toward the doorway. Their eyes went blank and their bodies ridged. Tune in tomorrow folks.

Moral or Morale

By Kent Humpal
Submitted on February, 2020

"But Marty, you out and out lied to them. You know we didn't have a trip planned for today," June said, as she unbuckled her seat belt.

"You know that I lied," says Marty, "And you know why I did it, but I don't feel right about it," he exclaimed.

"Well, it's too late now, unless you want to explain our change in plans," she replied.

"Well, I'm uncomfortable about it," he said. "You know what our minister said about lying. One lie leads to another and they often get bigger as they go on."

"Yeah, yeah, I know, but did you want to go on the 2-week long trip to Mendocino and live in their cabin?"

"No, not really, but they are our best friends. I feel guilty, telling a lie like that, and you took me by surprise when you did."

"Look," Marty said, "I would like to go to the cabin with Dave and Mary, but you know what she said. Her brother Robert and his wife would also be there. All he talks about is the next big deal he has going and how he has fleeced another client, and she brings up every ailment conceivable and how she knows she has it even though the dumb doctors can't diagnose her or explain her latest list of symptoms."

"Well, that's true. They both drive us up the wall," June agreed. "But during the day we're mostly outside hiking or photographing wildlife. They hardly ever join us."

"Yes, but what about the evenings? Robert gloats and chats over every trick he takes at Monopoly, but he always wins or he even gloats if he just lands on Park Place or Atlantic Avenue. And it gets worse, after the third or fourth drink."

"So, on the spur of the moment, I made up the trip were taking," Marty said. "Morally I feel bad, for we're letting our friends down on the basis of a grey lie."

"No, were not, said Marty. I'm calling the airlines tomorrow and making a couple of reservations for Boise. You've wanted to see your Mom and Dad anyway. You also have a new niece you haven't seen yet. And we can go to Cascade Lake or Silver City for a while as well."

"Well, your lie has turned into the truth. I guess I can live with that," June said.

Map Mishap

By Kent Humpal
Submitted on February, 2020

"We should have stopped at that Ranger Station. You never listen. You're so Bull-headed," Sheila remarked in a strained tone.

"We're not lost. The Google Map said to go eight miles to the Y in the road and then follow the road to Route #132. I haven't seen it come up yet, have you?"

"These maps are very accurate. They are taken from either an aerial or satellite photograph. Google then confirms them with a ground check."

"Well, I've been watching the odometer and we've gone way over eight miles. We're either lost or we're confused. We need to stop at the next campground or cabin for directions."

"I checked the US Forestry Map I picked up at last night's motel, and the flat topped bluff should be on our left, and not in front of us."

Digging through the control box between the seats she murmured that he was such a self-righteous fool, but here it is, Federal Bureau of Land Management, Topographical Map for Area #57.

Ralph glanced over and remarked, "I'll bet those maps are ten years old, and even though you just bought then at REI, they are probably out of date."

Unfolding the map, Sheila began searching for the last recognizable location. "Ralph, do you remember a cyclone fence with a Guard House barrier across the road?" questioned Sheila.

"I don't remember a Guard Post. We've been driving by a fence for a lot of miles. What about it?"

Ralphs voice expressed a growing agitation over Sheila's questions.

"Everything inside that fence is off limits to everyone but military and NASA personnel and to some Special Agency. I think we should turn around and go back."

"Oh, for Christ's sake, Sheila, we're not lost. Google says we're on track. Sheila pointed outside. Ralph, since we got on the wrong side of the fence, that bluff should be over there. The map shows it clearly. Just stop and look at it."

"Sheila, we're not lost. We said we would meet the other Coyote Springs group before night fall, and it's still early afternoon. Watch for their sign and let me drive."

"Listen to reason, Ralph, we're lost." Exasperated, she was getting soar and angry. Ralph pulled over to the side of the road. "All right, let's try to resolve this. Call our friends on AAA and see if one of us is right."

Sheila dug out her phone, hit fast dial, paused, and then she touched another number. "Ralph, I can't get anything. Look, there are no bars showing."

"That can't be right, for we're high and in the open, so let me see it."

He grabbed the phone and punched in the same numbers, but nothing happened. The phone pinged and a message came up. Turning around, they started back towards the main road. Fifteen minutes later they sighted a Humvee blocking the road. They pulled to a stop, when a camouflaged painted truck pulled up behind them. Armed soldiers stepped out of both vehicles as a helicopter came out of the sun and hovered overhead.

After a short, but intense conversation, and some not so subtle questioning, an officer on a radio talked to another officer. "No sir, we checked this car physically and did a magnetic and electronic monitoring of the vehicle. No evidence—I checked them out all ready?"

"Okay, it sounds like a domestic dispute—a severe case of male stubbornness said the female officer. Yes, sir, we will escort them to the nearest exit. Please follow the truck and we will get you on your way. You will find the road you want about twenty miles back. Move to the right, and you will see the numbered road. The copter steamed off to the NW and the Humvee disappeared on an invisible track."

"Well, Ralph, you were right. There was another way to solve the argument."

A Meth Head
For Their Madness

By Kent Humpal
Submitted on February, 2020

Stump and Ray-Bob stepped through the gates of the Bloom County Farm together. It hadn't been so bad. Some ditch and road work for three meals, a cot, use of some basketball courts, and TV. Thirty days was okay—kind of a vacation in fact. There was nobody telling them to get a job, to take their lazy butts off the couch, or to help with the chores.

Stump reflected on their experience. They'd both done shorter stints in various jails. Starting in Junior High, where they met, Stump and Ray-Bob were quite a pair. They began with petty theft and joy riding, but they gradually worked up the lists.

Ray-Bob eventually inherited his Grandpa's and Dad's Still, which had been upgraded through the years. That why he and Stump got 30 days this time, for they hadn't yet paid off the local authorities.

The Still was still working, but only for the McCracken's in Custer County.

"Oh well," sighed Ray-Bob.

Neither one ever liked school, but they weren't stupid—but were just always looking for the easy way out. Jail had been like a Junior College to them. They listened, questioned, and learned all they could while in the County Farm.

"Ray-Bob, what are we going to do? I'm not boosting cars any more, and you've got to work with the low lives and the strangers. The Still is gone, and we could replace it, but our customers have moved on."

"I know, I've been thinking about it for the last couple of weeks," Ray-Bob said.

A beat up Van pulled into the parking lot and a voice called out. "Get your no good criminal selves into my limo, men, for it's time to roll," called out slim Jim, another one of their crew.

"You boys look all right, so it must not have been too bad, for at least you got a meal and a place to stay."

Stump thought it over. "Well, my family doesn't want me staying with them anymore. They say it attracts too much attention."

Ray-Bob spoke up. "Listen, I've been thinking about something I learned at the Farm. It's going to take some studying, but I think we can make some big money out of it. Let's meet at the shack, where the old Still was. Since they took the still, there won't be any sheriffs or alcohol cops around there."

94

"OK, but why don't I just stay there. I'll get my sleeping bag and stuff. I'll just move in and my folks will be relieved," said Stump.

* * *

Meeting 2 days later, Ray-Bob, Stump, and Slim sat on the porch of the old shack. Ray-Bob, smoking a joint, leaned in and talked in a low voice. "You know a lot of the guys in the county jail talked about Meth making. It's a little dangerous but not if you take precautions. Look, we ran a Still. My whole family ran Stills. If we can do that then, you know our product was good, so why couldn't we make more money doing something else similar?"

"Well, yeah" said Stump, "But doesn't Meth making require chemicals and equipment?"

Slim entered the conversation. "You know LaVern, over by Satterfield. He had a friend who lived in one of those leased out state farms. The friend had the equipment for making Meth and said it was real easy."

"Then why isn't his friend making money today," asked Stump.

"Because he got killed in a car wreck on Whippoorwill road just before you boys went up. LaVern said the burners, propane tanks, and cookers were all hidden under the floor. He will go into this with us if we share the profits, as he wants to marry Ellie Ann Jenkins soon and he needs the money."

"Well, ok, but let's keep this talk to the four of us. The guys in jail gave me the names of people willing to take us up on it. If we don't want the stuff, all of it will eventually be sold to others."

* * *

A month had gone by and the first batch had been sold to a bunch of nasty mean looking people. Ray-Bob had done all the cooking himself, not trusting Stump to be attentive enough. The four had finally settled into a routine, where Ray-Bob did the cooking, Stump spelled off on the routine work including Guard Duty, Slim rustling up supplies which had been harder to procure, and LaVerne became a go between with the clients.

Ray-Bob was super cautious. He had gone on the Internet to check out stories. The fires and explosions were pretty common and deadly. Even the authorities wore Hazmat outfits and set up boundaries for the process. He used a face mask, fans, and opened windows and doors to keep the fumes outside the shack. The *No Hunting* or *No Trespassing* signs had worked so far, even though some of the staff had reported the chemical smells.

"Now, Stump, you've watched me do this over and over again, so do you think you've got it down now?"

"Well, I'm not dumb, Ray-Bob. I can learn what's important. Didn't I run the Still with my family on my own sometimes?"

Slim drove up with food about then and Ray-Bob put down the cans of chemicals before going outside to help them unload.

"Stump, you've got to be careful about mixing this stuff." Pointing to the cans of chemicals, he said," "You can mix can 1-A with the stuff in the bag marked 3-B, but as I've told you, don't skip a step and mix those two together in a hot boiler. They have to start out cold." He then walked into the other room to help Slim Jim.

Stump began working over the pots and large boilers. Hell, Ray-Bob was too cautious, he thought. Nothing can happen. He took the boiler off the gas burner, mixed the two chemicals together, and found the 3rd was ready, while getting hot in another bottle. He poured the chemicals from the hot kettle into the very warm kettle, and ....

KA-BOOM

As their spirits floated up through the flaming hot vapors into the atmosphere, Ray-Bob's voice could be heard – Damnit ....

I TOLD YOU NEVER TO DO THAT

An Apple A Day

By Kent Humpal
Submitted on February, 2020

They waited quietly in the lab, some optimistically, some pessimistically. They had been working on this experiment for months. A few had spent years speculating and pushing various ideas about time travel, teleportation, and other dimensions. Several had suffered ridicule, media harassment, loss of positions, and research grants. Now it was time for results from their recent attempt at teleportation.

They had tried solid, inanimate objects with some success, but small, living creatures were less successful. Various worms and larvae just plain disappeared. Starfish and mollusks did come back, but were dehydrated and dead upon arrival. Only cockroaches survived, but they died soon afterward.

Impatient grumbling began as time stretched on. Most did not leave their view of the small changer, hoping for the best, but preparing for failure. The machine began to buzz, and a barely visible beam appeared and centered on the porcelain bowl on the non-magnetic tray. Slowly the apple they had sent to an unknown destination reappeared.

"I told you so, when gasps of skeptics and relieved smiles began to appear in the assembled group. Finally, a technician who filtered the tanks, wearing protective gloves and a Hasmat apron, reached in and removed the apple. Jostling then began in order for all to get a better view, or to just touch the apple.

The need to verify that it was the same apple began immediately. This was satisfied finally by removing an inserted identifying granule and scanning it, along with some other scientific markers. Finally they all agreed on its authenticity.

As it was passed around the group in a protective glass container, someone raised it up to get a full view. There was definitely a small bite out of it. It's small but it looks like a human shaped bite with human shaped teeth indentures. A bright light and magnifying lens were produced. The forensic dentist and an anthropologist gave the mark a long look, conferred with each other, and announced that it looked humanoid, but we will need to make a more detailed examination and do further tests. Maybe even use DNA.

As the conversation and congratulations began to die down, one of the team called out, "Look, there's another beam coming down in the chamber."

Slowly a note in a very stylized, but clearly cursive letter came into view.

"What's it say? What language? Read it!"

The Linguist, Dr. Irene Vosges, took it out and then spoke to the crowd. "Well it's in English, French Chinese, Sanskrit, and some other unfamiliar language."

"Well, what does the message call out?" an anthropologist asked easily.

"It says, please send me only small apples, preferably tart and washed."

"Thank you."

Chuck Northup Stories

A Night to Forget

By Chuck Northup
Submitted on March 2020

"But Daddy, the Prom is the biggest event of the year at the high school, and everyone will be wearing nice clothes," pleaded Kathy.

"I agree," added her mother. "John, this dance is the beginning of her adult social life. She absolutely must look nice, just like everyone else. The boys will all be in tuxes, and the girls will all be in formals."

"Well, you're so good at sewing—why can't you buy some material and make a nice dress for her?" complained John.

"I can't because a formal dress is not a simple housedress. It requires yards and yards of special material to be right in order for Kathy, your daughter, to look good," explained Kathy's mother.

"Well, OK, but try to keep the cost down, will you. We've got lots of expenses this month, with the war and rationing and all that, and I'm having a tough time keeping the business profitable.

"And, by the way, young lady, who is the boy who is taking you?"

"Jerry has asked me. I've never gone out with him before, but I have a couple of classes with him. He seems really nice," answered Kathy.

"Well, bring him in when he comes to get you. I want to meet him," demanded John.

* * *

It was 1943 in Green River, Iowa. The local high school was providing the seniors with a prom during their last year in school. Students and counselors had been planning the event for months and were fixing up the gym with decorations. In addition, they had held a contest to elect a prom King, a prom Queen, and a retinue of courtiers. The winners of these coveted titles were usually the most prominent or most popular students who took part in several activities.

The prom was the most important event of the senior year. Students and their families spent quite a bit of money buying dresses, renting tuxes, buying flowers, and getting all the various other things that go into making a dance become a success.

"Dad," said Jerry. "I'm taking Kathy to the prom next month. Can I borrow your car for the night? Mine is a piece of Junk."

"Kathy? What happened to Melanie? I thought you two were going steady."

"Mel's grandma got sick, and she went to stay with her for a while in Oregon. I checked with her about the prom and she told me I could go with another couple with chaperones if I wanted to. I asked Kathy to go with me, and she agreed. We're in some classes together, so I know her a little bit. Now, can I count on the car, please?"

"Well, you know we only get four gallons of gas each week, so you won't be able to drive around much. You'll only be able to get Kathy, go to the dance, and then take her home again."

"But Dad, I'll have to pick up the other couple, and then go to a restaurant as well. But that won't be far," declared Jerry.

"Well, that'll be all right then—but no driving around—and that car better be clean when you return it. I expect you to get it washed and polished before you go. Is that agreed?"

"You bet, Dad. I want it to look great, too."

"OK, I'll agree, but you'd better not use more than one gallon of gas!"

* * *

The night of the prom, Kathy and her mother managed to get Kathy dressed and put real makeup on for the first time. Kathy had bought a boutonniere for Jerry to put on his lapel, and her mother had allowed her to put a dab of perfume onto her neck.

They then presented themselves to John, and he smiled all over. "You look positively beautiful, Kathy. You appear quite grown up. Martha, we have raised a gorgeous daughter.

"Be sure to bring in this young man when he arrives. I really want to meet him," he cautioned Kathy.

"I will, Daddy. I hope you'll be nice to him.

"Oh, I will. I just want to see him and tell him to take good care of my precious daughter."

Just then, the doorbell rang, and Kathy went to the front door. Standing there in his rented black tux with a black bow tie was Jerry, holding a box.

"These are for you to wear on your wrist," Jerry said, holding out the florist box.

"Thank you, Jerry," Kathy said, and opening the box she gleamed. "They are beautiful! Please come in. Daddy wants to meet you."

"Daddy, this is Jerry McManus, and this is my mother."

"McManus? Is your father the man who runs the hardware store?" her father asked.

"It's nice to meet you. Yes, and that's my father."

"I hope you two have a good time tonight. Please drive carefully—this is the only daughter we have. I told her she must be home by twelve."

"I will be careful, and I will get her home by that time," agreed Jerry. "We must be going now to get to the gym when the dance starts."

* * *

At eleven-thirty, Kathy opened the front door to her home, only to see her two parents staring at her. She looked very sad. Her hair was a little mussed, and her corsage was gone. Her shoes were muddy.

Her mother spoke first. "Kathy, I didn't hear the car. Where's Jerry?"

John didn't wait for an answer, saying, "You look bad, honey. Your shoes are dirty. What happened?"

Kathy sobbed, half-crying. "The prom was really great. Everyone looked their best with all the guys in tuxes and the girls in formals. There were lots of flowers, and the school had put up a ton of balloons and crepe paper. Jerry is a good dancer, and he is a good driver, but he got fresh and I didn't like that.

"We were supposed to have another couple with us, but that didn't happen—on purpose, I think. Instead of going to a restaurant like he said, he drove out to the drive-in movie and sneaked in. That's when his hands got busy. He told me he spent lots of money on this prom date and he wanted some necking in return. I told him, no way, got out of the car, and I walked home."

Her mother hugged her and added, "I'm sorry your prom date ended so badly. I'm happy that you kept your head."

John joined the hug and complimented Kathy on her behavior. "I'll go over to the hardware store tomorrow and speak to his father."

"Daddy, don't be too harsh. Nothing really happened. He didn't try to rape me—he just wanted to neck and kiss, and I didn't want to. Don't be too angry with his father."

"Jerry was impolite with you. He didn't do what he said he was going to do—engage another couple and go to a restaurant. That's enough reason to talk to his father. Also your most eventful evening was spoiled by him."

"Daddy, do what you will. I'm now going to bed."

Friday the 13th

By Chuck Northup
Submitted on March 2020

Quincy got up on Friday morning, and while heading for the bathroom he stubbed his toe. "Ow! I think I broke it," he said to his wife, Nancy.

"Let's put some ice on it. If it doesn't feel better in a while, I'll drive you to the Urgent Care to have it examined," Nancy said. "Anyway, I'll now go put some coffee on for us."

Quincy got dressed and headed out to get the newspaper. It had been raining all night—actually the first real rain after summer. As he walked through the front door opening, he spotted the paper lying in a puddle near the front steps. He reached down and picked up the soggy mess, murmuring, "Why doesn't that kid get the paper up on the porch where it's dry?"

Quincy was a photographer. He was able to sell his photos regularly to various magazines, and he earned a good living doing that. He had an assignment today to come up with a good photo of tonight's Harvest Moon—that's the full moon nearest to the Fall Equinox. This year it fell on Friday, the thirteenth, which was today. With all this rain, he won't get the shot he wanted and he will miss a nice assignment as well.

"Nancy, the paper is soaked. We'll have to spread it out somewhere to get it dry. How's the coffee coming?"

"It's not coming at all. The coffee-maker won't turn on. I guess I can boil some water and pour it through the coffee grounds."

"That'll be a bother. Just fix me some bacon and scrambled eggs, and I'll get some coffee at the office."

Quincy spread the newspaper out on the sofa and easy chair, got out the hair dryer, and started blow-drying it. He managed to read some of the headlines as he did this. One headline grabbed his attention:

Bankrupt Magazine Closes

He dried out that portion of the paper more carefully to see what magazine it was. He then shouted, "Hey, Nancy, *Good Looks* magazine went broke. That's the magazine I had my moon-shot commission with. Boy, I'm glad they didn't owe me any money. I never would have been paid for that shot if they had owed me."

He took part of the paper back into the kitchen to show Nancy—reading it as he went.

Magazines and newspapers all over the country are suffering from a lack of circulation, because of the internet and television coverage of news. This bankruptcy is simply another failure in a long line of failures.

110

"Nancy, no wonder why my business has fallen off. Maybe I'll have to find some other way to bring in money?" Quincy bemoaned, as he sat down to his breakfast.

"Gee, these eggs sure taste good. Thank you. This is the first good thing that has happened today. So far, Friday the thirteenth is living up to its superstitious reputation."

Before sitting down, Nancy thought she heard the postman rattle the mailbox, so she went out to pick up any letters she might find there. There was the usual batch of junk mail and a letter from her favorite cousin, plus a bill or two. She tossed most of it on the breakfast table, and opened the letter from her cousin.

Quincy ruffled through the junk mail and saw one from the Publishers Clearing House. It offered him $1,000 a week for life, as a prize.

"Here's what we need, Nancy," he said, as he looked up to see tears in her eyes. "What's wrong, honey?"

"Evelyn's husband had a heart attack and died," she said. "They had a funeral for him, but there's going to be a memorial service next week. I think I'll go, for Ev will need some comforting," Nancy sobbed.

Quincy got up and hugged Nancy saying, "That's a good idea. You go. I'll be just fine here. I've got plenty to keep me busy at the office. Be sure to give Ev my love."

Quincy went into his office. The accountant was going to be there today to take care of the books as he always did on a regular basis. Quincy greeted Arnold, the accountant, when he arrived.

"Arnie, it's good to see you. This day has not gone well so far for me. Lots of lousy things have happened already. What news do you have for me?"

"Quincy," Arnold said, as he pulled up a chair with a serious look on his face. "Your business is not doing as well as it should. I suggest that you help your profits by getting a smaller office, or close this one altogether, while working from your home. This place is eating you alive."

"Arnie, I need the darkroom space, but maybe I could convert a bedroom into one at home. Now that the kids are gone we have extra space."

"That would be a good way to save some money," Quincy. "Otherwise you may not last another six months, unless you inherit a bunch of money."

"Arnie, now that you mention it, what do you think of the Publishers Clearing House prize?"

"It's a come-on to get your name onto hundreds of mailing lists," replied Arnold.

"That wouldn't bother me, for I've got a big trash can. I think I'll answer the offer. What's to lose?" said Quincy.

"You'll be inundated with junk mail, that's what," laughed Arnold. "But, what the heck. Try it if you want to. You might get one of the prizes."

Quincy did move his business into a smaller space in a low rent area and put his darkroom in his home. Since the zoning regulations didn't permit business at his residence, he maintained a studio in the business district. He increased his advertising for studio work to compensate for the lack of outside sales to magazines.

Soon his business had grown enough with these changes, so he and Nancy stopped worrying about their income so much. Then one day, about six months later, they were both at home, he working in his dark room, and she doing some housework, when the front doorbell rang. Nancy went to the door to be greeted by a couple of people and a video camera man.

"Mrs. Phillips?" asked the woman.

"Yes," Nancy said haltingly. "Who are you?"

"We're from the Publishers' Clearing House. Is Mr. Philips in?"

"Just a moment, please." Nancy called over her shoulder. "Quincy, come out here immediately."

Quincy arrived at the door quickly. "What going on?" he asked.

The man at the door spoke up. "Mr. and Mrs. Philips—you are the winners of the grand prize of

$1,000 per week from the Publisher Clearing House. Congratulations."

The videographer was maneuvering his camera around to get better shots. Quincy had to grab Nancy as her legs suddenly failed her.

Quincy said, "You mean we've actually won?"

"Yes, and here's your first check," said the lady.

The two people were then invited in. There were lots of papers to sign and plenty of videotaping to be done. Eventually everyone had gone and Nancy and Quincy were left alone.

"Well, we aren't millionaires, but $52,000 a year won't hurt. Now I can reopen my larger office and we won't have to scrimp as much.

Friday the 13th turned out to be pretty lucky after all, and the full moon came up on a new life for them both.

First Impression

By Chuck Northup
Submitted on March 2020

Sam had a special opportunity to go to camp this summer. He was a seventeen-year-old Eagle Scout, and he had been to camp each summer since he was twelve. But this year was different. He would be a leader, stay the entire summer, and he would even be paid a nominal sum of money for the job.

Camp Firefly was regional. Boys who attended were Boy Scouts from several different troops in the region who stayed for only one week. Most of the campers were strangers to each other, but occasionally two or three from a troop would arrive at the camp at the same time.

The leaders were more stable. They were usually older boys with experience at this camp—so they knew the routines and customs and didn't need much training or guidance from the administrators.

All of the leaders shared a special building. Apart from the campers, each would share a dorm room with another leader, and each would have a communal bathroom to share.

There were eight leaders and two administrators. No one knew who they would be sharing a room with, but many were repeat campers, so the chance of sharing with someone they knew was quite possible. However, they had no choice in the matter of who they shared with, for that was up to the administrators, and Sam's roommate was meant to be a surprise for him.

Before he left home, Sam was busy for a few days preparing for the trip.

"Do you have a washer and dryer at the camp?" His mother inquired.

"Yes, I can take just enough clothing for a week and that way I won't have to pack as much," Sam replied.

"Then you had better take along some laundry soap—they may not have enough," advised his mother.

"Don't bug me, Mom. They furnish all that kind of stuff. Don't worry."

"Well, I do worry. You'll be gone all summer, and I wouldn't want you to run out of the essentials."

"Mom, this camp has been running for many years now. They know what they're doing. I'll be just fine."

* * *

The bus ride was about two and a half hours long, and Sam was picked up at the station by a camp van to take him the rest of the way. Along the way the driver, who was one of the administrators, told Sam, "You'll be staying with Fred Averele. Do you remember him?"

"No. He must have been at camp when I wasn't. What's he like?"

"Fred's from up north and he hasn't been to camp as many times as you. That's why we paired him up with you. And by the way, you'll be in charge of Tent number C. There are six boys in that tent," added the administrator.

"That's the tent I stayed in last year. I like that one because it's got a big shade tree by it, and it doesn't get as hot as the others."

* * *

They arrived at Camp Firefly after about a half hour drive up the mountain.

"Take your things over to the Leaders' cabin, leave them in room number 3, and then come back to the Headquarters to sign in. Your roommate is already there. You'll meet him when you take your stuff over," said the administrator.

Sam went to the Leader cabin, opened the door to room number 3, and saw someone leaning over his bedside, unpacking his suitcase. As soon as Sam entered, the other boy stood up and turned toward him.

Sam saw a very tall, lanky model smiling at him. He was blonde, with blue eyes that wrinkled at the

117

corners as he smiled. His smile was so broad that his teeth shone white between his parted lips. His face was soft and somewhat feminine, and his hair was carefully combed into a wave. His polo shirt was so form fitting that his muscular body was apparent. He seemed to be athletic. He wore shorts that were also form-fitting. He looked like he had just climbed out of a magazine ad.

Sam's immediate impression was that this fellow was gay, and was either a basketball or perhaps a tennis player. The gay part didn't bother him—after all there were lots of gay guys at school, but one sure didn't belong here at a boy's camp.

Sam interrupted his thoughts and greeted him. "Hi, I'm Sam. You must be Fred."

"Yes, I'm from Troop 87 in Bentley. I'm a senior at Bentley High. Where are you from?" asked Fred.

"I'm from Troop 39 in Temple. I'm also a senior, but I go to Wilson High. Have you been here often?"

"I've been here only once, but I attended camps elsewhere for three years before that. This is the first time I've been away all summer. I like the idea of having a summer job, but my girlfriend is very unhappy about me being gone. She's going to miss my close company, if you know what I mean."

Sam thought, there goes the gay bit, but he spoke up right away. "I don't have a steady to worry about. My mother is the one who will worry. She's been hovering over me this last week. Do you play basketball? You look tall enough."

"Yeah, but they'll have to get along without me this summer. I'm not so good that they will miss me anyway. Do you play?"

"No, I've played some, but my favorite is baseball when I'm not practicing my trombone," said Sam, as he extended his arm as though he was playing one.

Sam and Fred became good friends that summer. Sam admitted to Fred that he initially thought Fred was gay. "Fred said that always happens. That's the problem with being a blond model. He told Sam that since models make good money, he might want to become one."

A Name to Remember

By Chuck Northup
Submitted on March, 2020

As Lucinda grew up, her favorite uncle, on her mother's side, was so thoughtful that he never forgot her birthday, and he would send a gift every year. Uncle Roscoe, as he was called, lived far away on the East Coast, and Lucinda resided in California, but as a child, she would travel with her mother, and spend many vacations visiting him and his family.

When she married, her first son was a boy, so she named him Richard with the middle name Roscoe in honor of her favorite uncle. She continued visiting the East with Richard even after her husband had been killed in an accident. She received a settlement from the insurance company that enabled her to live very modestly, but she didn't know how she could pay for Richard's college education.

Lucinda's married name was Crossing, so her son's name was Richard Roscoe Crossing, and school kids would call him "Railroad Crossing." They would forever greet him with a train whistle, or a "Whoo-Whoo" sound, as they passed him in the hall.

What he and the other kids didn't realize was that the uncle he was named after was the son of the man who invented the ballpoint pen, so all of the vacations he and his mother took back East were spent at the seaside mansion of a very rich uncle. The mansion was located on one of the islands reached by boat off the coast of Georgia.

"Railroad" remembered the wonderful times he had at that location seeing the turtles, birds, and other wildlife on the island, and enjoying the sandy beaches surrounding it.

One day Lucinda received an unexpected phone call. It was an Associate from the offices of Bagby, Cason, & Farwell, Attorneys at law. He desired to make an appointment with Lucinda and Richard to discuss the will of her recently departed uncle.

This announcement came as a surprise because she didn't know that Uncle Roscoe had died. She then realized that she had not heard from him for some time.

"When did he pass away?" she asked.

"On the 10th of the month. We are just getting around to settling the will at this time. You are asked to be present when the other heirs hear the reading of the will. That meeting is planned for the 30th in Boston. Will you be free at that time?"

Lucinda thought for a moment, and then she said, "Yes, that would be convenient. Do you wish Richard to attend also?"

"Yes, both of you are mentioned in the will."

"I can take him out of school for a short time. How long should I plan on?"

"Probably for only one day plus your travel time of course. You may wish to stay overnight, so you might make hotel plans."

They settled the time and address particulars and then hung up. When Richard returned from school that day, she told him of the call.

"What do you think he left us?" asked Richard.

"Probably a sum of money. He always remembered me on my birthday. He probably left something for you as well. We'll find out when we get there."

They made their flight and hotel plans and took the trip. All the heirs gathered in the conference room of the law office, and Mr. Carson introduced himself.

"I am in charge of disposing of the will, so with that in mind, I will proceed to read it. Roscoe was a widower, so his estate was distributed to his children and a few others."

He proceeded with the reading, punctuated by oohs and gasps from the various heirs, as their share of the will was read. Roscoe had his hand in several businesses and real estate holdings and these were distributed to his children.

Toward the end of the will, the attorney turned to Richard and said, "To Richard Roscoe Crossing I leave my estate on the Georgia Island, to be held in trust by his mother Lucinda Crossing, until he is of age."

Richard gasped. Lucinda gasped. They stared at each other.

The attorney continued, "As a part of the processing of this will, this firm has determined the various values of each asset."

He then read off a list of assets and their values. The total assets were valued at several billion dollars, and the island estate alone was valued at $14,758,000.

When everyone left the law offices, Lucinda turned to Richard and told him, "We now have some plans to make. You college education is assured, and we can stop worrying about our income. Living without a husband, and you without a father, has been tough on me. Things will ease up a bit now.

Electroport

By Chuck Northup
Submitted on March, 2020

Weldon finished signing the waiver papers and stepped into the dressing room in advance of becoming nude and being transported 3,000 miles by electronic means. At the other end was a receiver bearing the same company named: Electroport—a somewhat new corporation that developed the method of transporting people over long distances in just a few minutes.

The idea is simple. Simply break down a person's body into electronic bits and send them to any place in the world that has a receiver that puts those bits back together again.

Weldon had seen others use this method of transporting with great success. It was far faster than airline travel. In fact, it was even faster than a rocket ship. One could go halfway around the world in moments. The major time was consumed in the breaking down and re-assembling the body bits.

Each of those processes required about fifteen minutes, depending upon the size of the person. Great care had to be taken in each process to be certain that each body organ remained complete and no body parts were left over.

Once a person stepped into the machine, he would disappear, leaving an empty capsule. In effect he would have died without a trace except for being received at the destination.

The receiving process was even more serious. Extreme care had to be taken in the "three-dimensional printing process." The human cell *ink* that was used had to match perfectly with each organ that it produced. This was accomplished by special DNA matching.

There were some drawbacks to the method. Color was obviously causing some concern. Matching skin or eye color was sometimes troublesome. Most people did not mind a slight change in their color, but if a major difference occurred, a customer was ready to sue. Disclaimers stopped that.

On rare occasions, major errors occurred. If a virus or malware happened at the time of the transport, no one knew what would come out at the receiving end. On rare occasions a person could end up with no liver or kidneys, or have an entire arm missing. These things simply became lost in space somewhere. The worst scenario was to produce a monster with strange body parts and organs that didn't work.

The brain was the biggest problem. Scientists spent more time researching this subject before coming up with an almost suitable result. Many customers found that they had lost their memory of many items, including their working skills. This made them useless to their company, and lawsuits almost always ensued.

Weldon stepped out of the receiving capsule and immediately went to the full length mirror. There he saw a strange man staring back at him. His eyes were no longer brown—they were a shade of green. His dark hair was now blonde. His ears were much larger and protruded outward from his head. His belly button was not in the right place—it was about three inches higher. However he was happy about one error—his genitals had become very much larger.

He dressed in clothing he had shipped ahead and found he was nearly two inches shorter, and two inches fatter, so his clothes didn't fit well. The Electroport Company was used to these occurrences, so they supplied him with new clothing for free.

Weldon got a taxi to his sister's home and rang the doorbell. When she opened the door, she did not immediately recognize her brother. All she saw was a stranger standing there.

"Marsha, don't you know your own brother?" Weldon asked her.

She replied, "You've dyed your hair and you've been eating too well. I didn't recognize you at first, but now I do. Come in and tell me what you've been doing."

Weldon and Martha spent a few enjoyable days together talking over old times and discussing his transporting. Weldon decided that he didn't want to chance any more changes on the return so he used an airline for his return trip.

In the next few months he had lost the extra fat around his middle, and some dye took care of his hair. He felt he could live with a different eye color or if he wanted he could use brown contact lenses. He also didn't mind his rearranged belly button, and he was extremely pleased with his very new and larger private parts.

Prospector

By Chuck Northup
Submitted on March, 2020

Ned liked to hunt for Native American artifacts, but the laws about picking up those articles are very restrictive in many places, unless one has a permit to do so. Ned applied for and carried those permits, and spent most of his summers prospecting about the areas where tribes used to camp or hunt.

These areas were usually in the states of Arizona, New Mexico, Nevada, and Colorado—near the Four Corners. The Navajo tribe was the largest and most populous one of that area, and they were very restrictive in allowing anyone to pick up articles, so Ned would usually avoid their territory. He also avoided private land whenever possible, but there were plenty of Federal lands to use anyway.

Ned was a modern day prospector. He would use his jeep to haul his camping equipment, then go out and set up a camp from which to operate. He took along a trailer with a mule so he would not have to carry heavy stuff around.

To be away from his camp would be to see an old prospector slouching along under a battered hat, leading his mule. He could stay out a few days at a time before returning to his camp, since his mule carried some food and water for himself.

Around his wrist Ned wore an up-to-date wrist watch that enabled him to locate the latitude and longitude of any location he desired. In that way he could mark out a spot anywhere by exact latitude and longitude, leave that place, and then return when he desired, without getting lost or losing his place. It also allowed him to stake out a claim if he desired. With the latitude and longitude, he was always within 100 feet of exactness.

One day, when Ned was about three days away from his camp, he located a place where tribes used to chip out arrowheads from flint. The spot seemed promising, because Ned saw many chip droppings scattered about in a relatively small area.

He told his mule, "Minnie, this looks like a work area. There are lots of small chips around here. Why don't we just mark this spot to come back to. We can get back to our camp and get more food. Then we can come back. What do you say?"

Minnie didn't answer, but Ned looked for his notebook to write down the location. It was not in the bag where he usually kept it. "I must have left it back at the camp. Minnie, what am I going to write on?"

Minnie still didn't answer. Ned looked all through his bags and couldn't find anything to write on. He looked all around his surroundings to see if there were any items he could use. The whole area was simply vacant of any growth—no bushes or trees. Then Ned had an idea. Ned took off his pants—then he took off his boxer shorts.

Minnie snorted. Ned checked his watch and took the latitude and longitude readings right down to the second and wrote them on his under drawers with a ballpoint pen. That solved the paper problem. Ned put his clothes back on and led Minnie back to the camp to replace their supplies. Ned found his notebook, and transferred the location into it.

The next time Ned washed his underwear, he discovered that his ballpoint pen used permanent ink.

Night Terror

By Chuck Northup
Submitted on March, 2020

"Time to get into bed," Maryann told her two girls after they drank their hot cocoa. "The School bus will come at 7:30, and you've got to get some sleep. When you're all tucked in, I'll come in and tell you a story."

The two ran off. They were seven and eight-and-a-half, but got along well together. They slept in bunk beds in the only other bedroom in the house that had belonged to their grandmother.

Maryann had inherited it, and instead of selling it, she decided to live in the old house until she could save up enough money to buy a newer one. Their father had died in a car accident last year, and they were left with only their mother to take care of them. It was not long before Maryanne heard them call out that they were ready.

Maryann read them a pleasant children's story about a little lamb that got separated for a moment from its mother, but was found again quickly. Maryann didn't like to tell scary stories at bedtime, for she didn't want the children to have bad dreams.

Maryanne had always been afraid of the dark. When she was young, she just knew that there was something hiding under the bed or in the closet. She didn't like dark rooms or walking down the sidewalk by herself at night for fear that something would jump out at her. Her imagination was always at the extreme.

When she married, all those fears seemed to calm down because she had a man next to her most of the time. But when he was away at work, those fears arose, even though her mind was now grown up, and she consciously knew that there really was nothing under the bed.

Now that she had no husband to cuddle next to her when she felt fearful, nights were still scary, and fears welled up in her more often. That night on the TV was a particularly poor set of events for watching. The wind was also bringing in a storm, and the old house was rattling.

The only things she could find to watch were action thrillers or shoot 'em up police and gang crime stories. After spinning the dial and becoming discouraged about finding a soothing story, she simply gave up and decided to go to bed.

She took a biography book with her, and propped up on some pillows to read. That was much more satisfying, and soon she was ready for slumber time. She nestled down into the soft comforter and cuddled her head down against the pillow, but the wind was still howling and rattling, so sleep came only after a long time.

There was much creaking in the house, and once she was even awakened by a puzzling sound of something falling. There was no night light because her husband could never sleep with one. The only light was the small amount that came in from the outside.

She lay awake wondering what had fallen when she heard a door creaking open. She guessed it was her bedroom door. She opened her eyes without raising her head, expecting to see one of the girls coming in. But, it wasn't. What she saw was a tall figure of a man. She bolted upright, clutching the comforter about her breast.

The room was so dark she couldn't tell anything about him except his size, which was big. But when the outside light caught him in its slight flow, she saw that he had something on his face that made him appear like a ghoul. She saw this horrible apparition and screamed in high pitched terror as the man slowly approached her.

Her daughters rushed into the room, snapping on the light, only to see their frightened mother sitting up in bed, grasping the blanket around her with white knuckled fists.

"It's all right girls. I just had a bad dream. Why don't you come and crawl into bed with me and make me feel better?"

Maryanne settled in with her daughters, and began to think that not only could these two girls use a father; she could use a husband. This may be a night to bring on a change in our lives.

Woman's Work

By Chuck Northup
Submitted on March, 2020

"Tony, it's a good thing you have work that doesn't take you away. Your real estate job allows you plenty of time at home."

"What are you talking about? Are you giving up living here, or something?"

"No, nothing like that. My sister just called and told me that our best friend in school had died, and there will be a funeral on Wednesday. She felt that I should attend since we were such good friends. I told her that I would."

"You mean, Martha, your sorority sister? She must not have been very old. I think you should go too. You two were very close. How long do you think you'll be gone?"

"Well, a lot of time will be spent getting there and back, and I'd like to spend a little time with Sis and catch up on our lives, so I'd like to be gone for a week."

"A week! I figured you'd be gone only for a few days. Who will take care of the kids all that time?"

"I felt you could handle it yourself. Your business allows you plenty of time, and they're in school most of the day."

"But that means I'll have to do the grocery shopping, the laundry, the cooking, and everything else by myself. How do you expect me to do all of that?"

"I do it every day. You just don't notice it. This will give you a chance to see what I do with my time while you are out selling homes."

"That sounds like payback time or comeuppance, but to show you I can do it. I'll take the challenge, and you can have a nice visit with your sister."

* * *

June was on the plane to Atlanta early the next morning. Tony saw her drive away and started breakfast, and the three kids were just getting up. That was an easy job for him because he did it every morning anyway. But this morning Nancy spilled orange juice all over her clothes and started to cry.

"Don't be upset, Nancy. We'll get you fresh clothes for school. Go into the bathroom and take off your dirty ones. I'll get fresh clothes for you and you can toss the wet ones in the laundry."

Tony made sure the two other kids had their food before he went to get fresh clothes for Nancy. He got her changed and back to the table when the others had almost finished.

"Make sure Nancy eats her breakfast while I fix your lunches. June usually did that chore, but he knew what everyone liked and he finished their lunches barely in time for them to catch the bus. As they went out the door, Tony said, "That went smoothly. I knew I could do it."

He put the dirty clothes into the washing machine, and while they were cycling, he did up the breakfast dishes—then he went back and put the clothes in the dryer. When he took them out, he found that they had shrunk badly. He didn't read the label and had used too hot of a setting. They were ruined so he threw them away.

The phone rang about mid-morning. It was the school. They wanted him to come down and talk with the principal. When he arrived, his son was in the office looking very sheepish.

"Your son has bullied another boy, and we want it stopped," said the principal. "I suggest you meet with the counsellor and talk things out. His office is just down the hall. You can go there with Jason now."

"What'd you do, Jason?"

"The other kid told me you were just a dumb salesman. I didn't want to hit him, so I just pulled off his backpack and threw it across the room."

"Let's go down to the counsellor's office and talk about it to him."

The other boy was brought in, apologies were exchanged, and the affair was over. Jason returned to class, and Tony went home feeling he had settled another problem successfully.

On the way home he decided to stop for groceries. He went through the aisles taking items off the shelves that he recognized were used at home. He didn't use a list—he simply filled his basket with stuff.

When the kids came home from school, they went straight for the fridge.

"Where are our smoothies?" Tony heard clearly in the living room.

"What smoothies do you mean?"

"Mother always made us fruit smoothies with yogurt. She said she had run out of low-fat yogurt and she had put it on the shopping list."

"I didn't have the list when I went to the store this morning. Can you snack on something else? How about a banana?"

"I don't want a banana—I want a smoothie!"

"I'm sorry I didn't get the yogurt. Isn't this the day you clean your rooms?"

Jenny went pouting off to her room and slammed the door. Tony looked at the other two who were watching and said, "I'll go to the store tomorrow and get some yogurt for you all so you can have your smoothies. Can I fix some hot chocolate for you now?"

"That would taste good," said Jason.

"Jason, when you're finished, would you mow the lawn please. It's getting long. And Nancy, help your sister clean your room. I have to start dinner."

Tony had a difficult time getting the kids to go to bed that night. He didn't realize that their mother had promised they could stay up and watch a special program on TV. There was lots of whining, but he finally relented and let them stay up.

The next morning, Jenny complained that her stomach ached and she wanted to stay home from school. Tony agreed she could if she stayed in bed. But later, he got a call from her teacher who said that Jenny had missed an important test.

There was a long discussion about Jenny's schoolwork getting worse, and that perhaps there was something else going on in her life to cause it.

Tony took the opportunity of Jenny's "sickness" to talk to her about school. He found that she had not been doing homework lately, and she didn't know the subjects very well. Tony wanted to delve into it a little deeper, but he decided he was in over his head and should wait until June came home.

That afternoon became medical day. Jason cut his thumb while playing with the neighbor and needed antiseptic and a band aid. Nancy fell off her bike and skinned her elbow. She came crying into the house and needed comforting, along with some washing up and bandaging.

"Your mother could do this better. I wish she were home," Tony told Nancy, as he wrapped up her arm in gauze."

"So do I," Nancy replied.

"This will feel better in a few days. There might be some slight bruising, but we can cover it up with long sleeves so no one will notice."

With these things going on, Tony forgot to go to the store to get yogurt, so the next day the same problem arose.

That night he got a call from June. She said it was a lovely funeral, and everyone was just fine.

Tony tried to put on a confident appearance but finally admitted that he was under water in problems.

"Could you cut your visit short and please come home? I really need you?"

Broken Glass

By Chuck Northup
Submitted on March, 2020

San Francisco tracked 1996 car break-ins in January 2019 alone. Unreported break-ins are not tracked. This rate has been going on for a year at least without any letup. The police are unable to stop this crime. It is happening all over the entire city, but is concentrated in heavily tourist spots near Golden Gate Park, Lombard Hill, and other tourist places of interest.

The crime lasts less than three minutes—one minute is most unusual—so the thief is gone before anyone can identify the culprit or even see him, because it is a smash, grab, and run operation.

The car owner's insurance may pay for the windows, but the deductible often is too high, so the owner pays for the damage himself and may not even report the theft. The police are unable to arrest the thief in 98% of all incidents, so they leave a very black mark on tourism in the city. The Council is presently considering paying directly for the loss to residents— not to visitors.

There is more than one way to identify the thief. In order to do so, the police must lay a trap. A good-looking Automobile can be parked in a likely place. A special package is then left on the front seat, and the car is locked and left alone. The special package is a trap. It is really a device that sprays a cloud of yellow dye toward anyone who picks it up.

When a person breaks the car window and reaches in, grabbing the inviting package, the trigger mechanism on the base of the package activates a hidden spray nozzle in the box that releases its colorful identifying spray toward the reaching thief. The thief may get away, but when he attempts to get rid of the covering color, he cannot. He will have many questions to answer, and eventually he probably will be reported to the police.

That scheme eventuality may never occur, so the police have another trick up their sleeve—the hidden camera. Along with the surprise package, a hidden camera is secluded in the center console of the automobile. When the box is first touched, the camera starts taking its video of the theft.

Lights on the camera will illuminate the entire action for a permanent record for any court action. The lighting can be installed in a separate location so the thief will not know where the camera is located, therefore making it unavailable for theft.

Several of the junkier automobiles can be parked throughout the city. Pictures of the thieves may be posted in newspapers or on posters for all to see. Any prospective thief will wonder if this next car is one of the traps. Not all junkier autos are bad looking, and packages can have all sorts of different appearances and still be inviting.

There is yet another method of actually catching the criminal. It is called the Bola Wrap. This is a new device shot from a distance, causing a very loud bang, and sending a Kevlar rope around the ankles of a culprit. It is harmless, but it stops the culprit in his tracks, without injury or pain.

This device could be attached under the trapping vehicle to retain the thief until the police can arrive. The Bola Wrap would be activated by anyone breaking the window. An automatic signal can be sent to any nearby police car to enable the officers to catch the thief in action.

As you can see, there is more than one way to catch a thief.

Betty Stearns Stories

My Sister and I
By Betty Stearns
Submitted on July 2020

Much to our surprise, my sister Ernestine and I received a letter from the mayor of Shingo, Japan, where we grew up. Inside we discovered an invitation to celebrate the gift of our childhood home to the city of Shingu. This was an opportunity we could not pass up!

So, here we are, joining the celebration back in our hometown. Although we had been gone for more than 70 years, the living room looked the same to us. The fireplace was still between two bookshelves and two French doors on the other side of the room.

Many beautiful speeches had been made to honor our parents, Ernest and Katherine Chapman, the first Residents of this house, and Isaku Nishimura, the architect of our home. I nudged Ernestine. "It's now time for us!"

Ernestine, using very proper and correct language, full of "honorifics," thanked the city mayor and Mr. Seki, the President of the Chamber of Commerce and the Historical Society, for this wonderful celebration. (Mr. Seki, it turned out, would host us through our entire visit to Shingu, arranging for trips to historical sites, and shrines, while boating us down the river.)

I interrupted her formal speech with the colloquial Japanese of the region. I pointed to my sister, "This is my little sister, "Mitchan," then pointed to myself, "I am Betty Chan." Then I pointed to the sky to "Meri Chan," my sister, who had passed on. ("Chan" was always added to a child's first name.)

"We have become very, very old, but long, long ago ("Mukashi-mukashi, oh mukashi") this house was our home. Many of our little friends came to play, calling at the front door, "Meri Chan—Asabore!" (Mary, let's play!) They always used the oldest sister's

148

name, meaning anyone would do. We loved the Japanese children's games—Ojami (bean bag), jump rope, taking over countries, stealing sandals, etc.

We ended with a low bow, as they clapped and laughed, delighted that these two very old ladies travelled from so far away to join in the celebration.

Just then the mayor and two distinguished looking men came toward us. I whispered that I thought it was time for us to cut the ribbon. They led us to the front yard. Instead of scissors, all five of us were handed golden shovels and instructed to start planting two little trees.

Flash bulbs went off as various newspaper cameramen arrived. Every time we put down the shovels someone would say, "Here's another newspaper, so please keep digging."

We felt like quite the celebrities. It was a day full of laughter, love, and adventure. We knew the mayor's banquet was awaiting us for the evening's festivities.

ASABORE!

The Unexpected

By Betty Stearns
Submitted on July 2020

I am gazing at three tiny stones on my desk—tiny, but full of laughter, love, adventure and beauty—they are tiny, but huge. I brought them home from a recent trip to Japan to celebrate the giving of my childhood home to the City of Shinghu.

Stone 1:

The largest of the three stones is shiny and black and just the right size to fit in the palm of my hand. I picked it up on the banks of the Kumano River (Bear Field)—a river that related so much to my childhood. On special occasions, we, as a family, would ride boats powered by old airplane propellers up this river. We also often hiked up to the highest point of a castle. From up there we could look down and see the Kumano river flow from the gorge (Doro Hatcho) alongside our town, Shinghu, under a bridge and into the vast Pacific Ocean.

Doro Hatcho is a most beautiful place with cliffs and wild azalea on either side. On our trip, it was our group's first choice for sight-seeing, but because of climate change, boat travel was impossible.

Our childhood home, now called the "Chapman House," was right in the midst of this Kumano Area. When I was little, there was no gate in front of the house. Mothers enjoyed sitting on the warm pavement, right in front, watching children at play. Now they would see a newly installed large gate with my father's signature carved in wood right above "Chapman House". I thought to myself, "My father was so loving, so loved, so very, very, humble, how would he feel, if he could see this gate now?!"

Stone 2:

I found Stone 2 on the ground near a temple while walking around Ninooka. This stone was brown and much smaller than Stone No.1. I immediately scratched "N" on it so I would not forget where I picked it up. Ninooka used to be a little village of trees and summer cottages where missionaries came for a few summer weeks for a well-earned rest. It was heaven for us children—playing with other friends and loving the small swimming pool. We, of course, did not have chlorine, so the pool water gradually turned warm, and green, and a little slimy. Just as it was feeling so comfortable, our fathers suddenly decided it was time to drain and scrub the algae out. Then the water was too cold for us and we could not wait for it to get warmer again. There were many other exciting and fun adventures for us kids.

We could not find these summer cottages as we remembered them. Now Ninooka is a beautiful bright red Buddhist temple, with a green lawn surrounded by two-story condos. Although our cottages were gone, there remained the same three enormous rocks where we used to play games with my mother. Stone No. 2 will always remind me of Ninooka, and those wonderful times. From Ninooka, we always had a perfect view of Mt. Fuji, the place where I found Stone No. 3.

Stone 3:

The third stone is black, rough and obviously volcanic. We took a bus up Mt. Fuji to the 5th Station. When we got off the bus and started walking toward the plaza, I found Stone No. 3.

I remember as a 12-year-old, climbing Mt. Fuji— we climbed all night with billions of stars above and pure silence. Station 5 is towards the bottom of the mountain. At that time, it was a hut. An old man gave us a cup of green tea and a little tatami (straw mat) where we could stretch out. My father and I were the only ones there that night. While we hiked, we only saw one or two other climbers, and at the top, there were about eight people there to greet the sun as it rose.

Now the 5th Station is a crowded plaza with many stores and gift shops. There were tourists from around the world with cameras out ready to take pictures of Mt. Fuji. But we could see nothing but white clouds.

It seemed quiet. Everyone waited, in anticipation that Mt. Fuji would appear. And then suddenly, the clouds parted, and we could see the enormous Mt. Fuji all the way up to its top peak. There were thousands of "Oh's" and "Ah's" and clicking of cameras.

Now, I reach for the tiny stones on my desk, put them in my pocket and take a walk.

Twenty Minutes

By Betty Stearns
Submitted on July 2020

I am sitting in a taxi, trying to relax. This seemed to be a better way to go than to drive myself through heavy traffic. I tried thinking of my father's wise words just before my dental appointment, when there was no Novocain to use. I remembered that in 20 minutes it will all be in the past!

But this is different. My family does not know that I have an on-line serious boyfriend who might possibly become my husband someday. We have been having wonderful conversations. We have discussed our values, or faith, our love of nature, our love of families and children, and our enjoyment of sports.

It's hard for me to believe but these conversations have been going on now for two years, but always by phone. We have never met face to face and have never discussed our appearance, and we're about to meet for the first time.

I am tall – 5 feet and 8 inches. I also have tattoos on my right arm and hand surrounding the words "I love Harry." (Harry was my high school boy friend).

My thoughts were interrupted by a stop sign. As I looked at my watch, it said 4 o'clock. No! In 20 minutes now all of this will be in the past! Just then my cell phone rang.

"This is your mother. Where are you? I've been trying to find you. I just got the strangest phone call from a weird sounding man. He said ask your daughter if an old tattoo would be ok."

I cried, "Yes! Yes! And I burst into tears! (Happy Ones).

Betty Wyatt Stories

The Dream Catcher

By Betty Wyatt
Submitted on November, 2019

It was a hot, humid Wednesday in October. Joyce had never been so weary. She had not slept again last night. Breakfast coffee had not perked her up at all. The girl on the desk called to her, "You have a package, Joyce. It looks interesting."

Joyce strolled to the desk. She couldn't imagine who would be sending her anything. It must be one of those "Free Prizes" that turned out to be dish towels. No, it was from the Phoenix First American Museum, with Naomi's name scrawled above the address.

"Thanks, Shira, I'll open it upstairs, but I'll let you know if it contains a treasure."

She had just talked to Naomi on Sunday. What could she be sending so quickly after their long conversation about Joyce's fatigue and failure to sleep this month, in spite of a myriad of trials by her Primary Care Doctor, who had now sent her to a hypnotist? Joyce had little confidence in all of that.

Once in her apartment she tore open the package and opened the small box. Inside on a pad of sheepskin nestled a Dream-Catcher and a note. "This is not a tourist trade cutie; rather this is the real thing. Isn't it gorgeous? Believe in it, and you will sleep." Love, Naomi.

It was lovely—a perfect circle of twisted branches bound with yarn of a multitude of colors that created a web across the circle and pendant in the center, which was a moonstone.

Joyce knew exactly where that moonstone had come from. She and her husband had discovered the mesa while studying native plants. She had a bracelet they had Tom Bhatti make from the stones they gathered that day.

She cradled the Dream-Catcher in the sheep skin and studied it closely, looking for a maker's mark. These serious catchers were usually made by women of the tribe in sacred ceremonies. They won't catch the lottery or a Ferrari for you but will work on the essence of problems you may have and not even realize it.

She walked to her bedroom and hung the Dream-Catcher from the head of her brass bed. All afternoon she felt lifted, as if a positive force had entered the apartment. She had been worried for over a month about the possible re-occurrence of her cervical cancer that had ended her child bearing days in her 30's. Afraid she would never see her grandchildren as more than toddlers and never know how her kids really turned out, had she done a good job or not? How had she failed as a Mother?

That night after the evening News, she went to the bedroom. The Dream-Catcher was catching the light from the hall with its silver and gold twine and the moonstone glowed. She took her night pills and did her night routine and slipped on her night gown, walked out to turn off the hall light, came back to say her prayers, and slide into bed.

An hour later she was still awake. Then a familiar theme began on the Classic music radio channel she used to sleep by. It was a song she knew from her choir days..."*When I lay me down to sleep, 14 angels* round me keep, two up on my right stand, two beside my left hand..." and so it went, with the recording repeating the theme several times, but she didn't know that she had fallen asleep.

The dark walls of the bedroom became a glade. Tall trees gave shade and a radio sat on a picnic table playing classical music. It was a big family picnic and she slowly realized these adults were with children, her kids all grown up with families of their own, and even the babies were born to her grandchildren. The new kids were playing volley ball and her children were setting the long pulled together picnic tables with food drawn from ice chests and baskets.

She could only spot her own children and their spouses and was trying to line up which young people belonged to whom. But where was Bob, her middle child? Then she heard her daughter-in-law speaking to one of the teen agers. "Yes, Dora, it is too bad that Dad is missing all the fun, but he should be home from Afghanistan in November and be back being a civilian Dad again. Just keep him in your prayers, as we all do."

Her Bobby in a war zone! That was worse than her worst dread. Just then a car pulled up at the curb. The driver exited and took a walker out of the back, brought it to the front, and helped an elderly lady into the walker. The man was John, her first born. He looked so mature and well groomed. How he had changed. He pushed the elderly woman toward the picnic tables. A shout of "Hi Grandma!"

rose from the group. Joyce glanced at the woman's hand. It was hers.

She was wearing Joyce's engagement and wedding band. As she reached the table, the group of 20 plus surrounded it. Starting with John on her right, they gave their name and a brief greeting. Finally her daughter, Naomi, who was named for her best friend, spoke.

"This is our first family reunion in many years and we are pleased to report that the entire tribe is here, even your newest great grandchild, Timmy. Bob is not here in the flesh, but he is on all of our phones," and John handed his to her. She saw a very handsome young man in combat fatigues with double bars on his shoulders, for he was a Captain. She burst into tears of happiness as they began to sing Happy Birthday to her.

The dream faded, but she slept on, and on, past the dawn which was golden and almost till noon. The dream remained in her memory for that day and many years to come. The Dream-Catcher became her dearest possession for wiping her fears away. It had worked its magic, for gone was the fear of recurring cancer, and gone was the fear of death. It was going to be OK.

Up A Creek

By Betty Wyatt
Submitted on November, 2019

Kim had been kayaking the river all day. When she started there were ten in the group, and when they reached a swimming hole near the campground, the group began to break up. She took a dip with the group and ate a snack with them and then went back on the river with three of her friends. An hour later they reached the area of the State Park where her friends had left the car and peeled off the River.

They offered her a ride back to San Jose with her kayak in the back of their pickup, and that would mean four on the bench seat that was meant for three. Too long for a crowded ride, so she declined with thanks and they looked a little grateful when she said "It's not too far to the first town, and I'm sure I can make it before dark. It's July and it stays light pretty late."

The solitude had been great. The river is wide and smooth. The trees on the banks had changed through the day from Aspens in the morning to Alders and now they were Sycamores and Cottonwoods.

An hour downstream the river was filled with large boulders, the tailing of a long ago landslide from the cliffs, and they were tricky to navigate. Then came the dreaded sound of a rip in the bottom of the bow. She could feel the water rushing in, so she steered as close as possible to the shore, hoping she would make it before the kayak sank. She lucked out, when a spur of shore stuck out of the water and she went aground only three feet from the shore.

She pushed up and out of the seat, grabbed her backpack and first aid kit from the bow, and a knapsack with her used stuff from the rear behind the kayak seat, which she tossed ashore. It landed in a massive stand of poison oak. The small shoreline was surrounded by her worst fear in the out of doors. She was a blue eyed blonde and the poison oak would turn her into a swollen red monster.

She left her gear in the small landing area that was clear and walked the narrow strip of land between the poison oak and the river. A larger cleared beach was ahead and she moved the kayak by her belt to the new area and made another trip to bring her back pack and other gear.

Somehow she had to let someone know of her plight. Searching her back pack she found no notebook and remembered using it back at the swimming hole where she lost her phone. No way to write or call anyone.

What to do. She looked at the wounded Kayak. The lining was whitish on the underside of the cover. She dug out her Swiss Army knife and cut a large strip about nine inches wide and a foot or two long. Digging into her back pack she found an eyebrow pencil and a tube of lipstick. With the eyebrow pencil she wrote on the light grey covering, "Stranded and up a Creek. Need help. Kayak torn and useless. No phone. Kim Cains, 16 Georgia Way, San Jose, CA, 90455. 1-408-333-6633. Female, 50's. Writer, nature articles. Please help me!"

Digging in her other knapsack she found the towel she had used at the swimming hole and the empty ten inch high plastic jar that had held the energy drink, now totally consumed. She washed the jar in the creek and dried it. Turning the whitish side of the kayak strip up, she took the lipstick and wrote "HELP" on each end. Rolling it carefully, so as not to smear it with the Help on each side of the jar, she now screwed on the lid and pushed it into the water. It floated beautifully and she saw it bounce off a couple of rocks, so the plastic was better than a glass bottle. Now to hope someone would spot it before dark.

Next, she needed a visual sign. There was a lot of debris at the shore line—twigs, branches, and one nice little log. She gathered some of the smaller boulders to make a fire ring. Then making a teepee of her twigs and other fuel and stuffing a piece of the kayak cover into the teepee, she got the lighter out of her first aid kit and sniffed several bottles looking for the most alcoholic in odor. Pouring it on the kayak cloth and brightening the edge, it flamed up beautifully and the twigs and sticks began to burn.

She scurried about the short gathering and looked for larger pieces and burnable greens to burn and send up smoke. The smoke rose nicely above the height of the trees and she hoped it would catch someone's eye. She took off her wet socks and stuck them over a fire ring rock to dry. She dried her feet and put on the dry socks she found in her back pack.

She heard the faint ker-flik of a helicopter, but it didn't come her way for about an hour after she had tossed the jar in the river. Had someone seen it? She was getting low on fuel, so she went along the narrow shore edge this time gathering sticks and twigs and anything she thought would burn or smoke in the empty knapsack. When it was bulging she made her way to the fire ring.

She was very hungry. The energy product in the now floating jar had long ago worn off. She dumped out the usually neatly packed back pack, which was now a jumble. She searched through everything, even pockets, and shook all of her crumbled clothing for something—anything to eat. Finally she found a crushed nature bar. She tore it open carefully over a cup to catch any crumbs and picked carefully by finger pinch until it was gone. Then, living dangerously, she drank some water direct from the creek.

She thought of all her mistakes in packing for this little trip. A lighter, but nothing to really make a fire with, she had lucked out with a hand sanitizer with high alcohol content, but nothing for poison oak, no tablets to purify water, no toilet tissue or extra notebook to write a journal. No extra writing implements—it went on and on.

Had Donald always packed their sacks so they always had the right stuff? Perhaps her solo days were over. What if she wasn't found by dark? Her little clearing had many tracks in its sandy soil, but she hadn't identified them before she walked all over and dragged things across it, so there was no chance now.

Then, as she grew more depressed at the mistakes on this kayak adventure, she heard the distant sound of an outboard motor approaching very slowly. Someone had seen the plastic bottle. Or maybe they were coming to check the smoke pillar which was ascending more vertical with dying down of the wind, as night was beginning to draw near.

The sun was almost ready to set when the small motor boat came in sight. They had a bull horn and called to her. She yelled back but couldn't be sure they heard her. They put into shore before the boulder area and waded up to her. She couldn't help it. She threw her arms around the two men in joy and relief.

One was an old timer who obviously knew this river and its hazards. He headed straight to the kayak. He picked it up to drain it and pulled the lever that folds it in half. The other was a college kid studying native plants with the older man this week. Kim put her boots back on, dumped her knap sack and turned it inside out to use as a water bucket and the kid fetched it from the river and drowned the fire. He made two trips with the rubberized container to be sure the embers wiped out.

She gathered all her gear and put on her back pack. She stuffed the knap sack after drying it out and slung it from her belt.

"Where's the paddle?" the older man asked.

"I used it as a poker for the fire, but it still is a paddle," she answered, retrieving it.

He stuffed it in the folded kayak. Then they all walked the site, making sure no debris was left and waded into the shallow toward the boat.

"Pleased to meet you, Miss Cains. I enjoyed your article in Landscapes of the West last month. Professor Steggins recommended it to the class. That's why we recognized your name in the bottle message. We phoned to find out if your message was not just some kid's prank, which it wasn't. I'm Tony Alvarez."

The older man introduced himself as they were starting downstream. "Mark Stebbins. I'm at Cal Santa Cruz. I enjoy your blog, Ms. Cains, but I urge you to proof your next SOS. You said you were stranded up a creek and we've been searching every creek that joins the river for two hours. We even brought in a helicopter."

"This is a river, Ma'am," and he laughed. So did Tony. She just grinned and shook her head—another error on this trip. Yes, it was time to give up on solo trips.

A Canoe to Adventure

By Betty Wyatt

Submitted on November, 2019

Bird watchers come in many variations—bird feeders, bird listeners of various species heard, as well as a long list of birds they have seen from all over the world. A sub-species of this type of birds is the Ticker (as the British call them) or a chaser. They chase new wild birds where they are reported on the RBA (Rare Bird Alert). It may be in a local park, or in the Everglades of Florida—they go and when they get there they meet up with other chasers. It's their idea of fun and can become a passion—like golf for more stable people.

A wild rumor on the RBA had brought Helen to this bayou in Louisiana. A party of this State's best Birders reported the sighting of an Ivory Billed Woodpecker in this area. Many such types of birds still popped up, although that bird is generally believed to be extinct in the United States and has not even been reported in the remnant population in Cuba for some time.

It was just a fluke that Helen was in Louisiana, when the report of the sighting possibility popped up on the Rare Bird Alert last night. She was in New Orleans on a buying trip for her Boutique in Palo Alto, and she was available to chase. She was an avid birder with an ABA list of 750 species.

When she called the Louisiana Fish and Wildlife last night she was given some detail of the possible sighting and the names of some people to call. One was a birder she knew from some tours together, so she knew she had transport to the site. To prepare herself, she shopped for boots at an all-night hardware store that had a tiny sporting goods section plus a section for a backpack and jeans.

* * *

Here she was on the banks of a cypress swamp, waiting to get a boat ride to a miracle, or if it was just another wild wood-pecky chase. All the birders gathered here in the pre-dawn were local, and many had their own boats for the shallow bayous. The larger boats were mostly full and because of her local contacts she had gotten a ride in a 40-seat, hollow log canoe. There were two Cajun crewmen aboard, one who stood in front to push debris out of the way and the other who was in the rear to pull the boat along when needed.

The sun was up when they finally pushed off. This was her second major canoe trip. The other one had been on a big lake in Michigan in a fragile birch-bark canoe, buoyant and light, when she was a 14 year old Girl Scout. There was no similarity at all.

When in the shade, the waters of the bayou resembled split pea soup. It was thick looking and full of minute particles of green that made it appear opaque. The kneed-Cyprus was exotic and other worldish. They stood on legs out of the water and the branches hung down to trail the Spanish moss in the water. Some trees were almost covered with it. When the sun shone, it looked like all those little particles were flecks of gold.

No matter how hard or fast we paddled, we moved slowly. The canoe was a heavy log. We sat deep in it and there was a guard rail attached to the top of the sides where oarlocks could be inserted in deeper water. It was primitive and had been hollowed out by fire, not by carving.

Everyone had been ordered to move as quietly as possible—no chatter, and no shouting. We were to use phones to communicate from boat to boat, so we had a linking number. Anyone sighting something was to communicate to the lead boat that would immediately put out information to everyone else.

Helen had never been in such a situation. It was eerie, plus the boats had scattered into various creeks that flowed into or out of the bayou. Two hours of nothing but silence, and then trouble for Helen's canoe. They were stuck in a shallow. The crewman in front ordered seat one and three to go over the side and push in order to help the crewman in back.

Helen was in seat three, so it was up and over the side for her, stowing her paddle beneath the seat. The surface was slick mud and lumpy with tree roots. They pushed on the count. Helen's boots were caught on the roots and down she went into the green guck, now muddied by their pushing. She struggled to free her right boot, and then to get up.

Two here-to-fore unseen alligators emerged from the reeds, dropped from the banks, and then headed toward the canoe. By the time the Cajun crewmen pulled the boat forward, one of the alligators was only one foot from her trapped boot. As the boat moved forward, her boot came free from the roots. The front pole man poked at the roots and Helen's boot popped loose and she was up and over the side, and into their boat.

Soaking wet and muddy, she sat in the floor of the canoe, breathing deeply. Then she shed her boots and drained them. The gators were still cruising behind them, but her pushes that lead to the fall had scooted them into more floatable waters. She retrieved the paddle from under her seat, got to her knees, and then slid into her seat. She had never been so scared in her life. Suddenly she didn't care if there were a flock of ivory billed woodpeckers in the bayou.

She wanted to go home!

A Whirl Wind Beginning

By Betty Wyatt
Submitted on October, 2019

It was not a really nice day at the beach. A sharp off-shore wind had come up and was whipping up white caps on the waves. Surfers and swimmers had mostly come out of the water and many of the people who had been playing games or who were stretched out to get the sun, were now gathering their gear and heading to their cars. Gary had been thinking about doing it too.

The bikini clad girl on the next towel had come in from the choppy water and was drying off, preparing to slip into some going home trousers and top. She was facing the surf and away from the dune behind them. Suddenly a rather large dust devil—no, you had to call it a very large sand devil,—topped the dune and headed for the beach.

It was the largest one Gary had ever seen and he yelled at the toweling girl to "RUN," but she didn't hear him, because of the rumbling noise the mini tornado was making as it scooped up debris from the beach. So, when she finally saw it, it was too late. The 20′ tube knocked her down and hovered a moment over her prone figure, but she was heavy enough that it couldn't lift her. A child might have been a different story, however.

He ran to her across the 30 feet that had saved him from the sand devil which had turned after knocking down the girl and headed down south in the sand, avoiding the wet sand that might have killed it.

Kneeling beside her, he asked if she was OK and what her name was. An answering groan of "My eyes, my eyes … my name is Debbie."

"Don't open them. I'll be right back." He sprinted back to his gear and grabbed the gallon thermos jug of water he had brought to stay hydrated for the day. It was too much, but he thought he might have met someone who needed it too. Well, he had. He added a towel and went back to the girl who was now sitting up.

A woman from up the beach who had collected her things and headed to her car when she saw what happened was comforting the girl. When Gary got there, he tore the towel in half and soaked it in the water. Making a cool compress of it, he took her hands from her eyes and began squeezing water into her eyes. Sand was washing out of the lashes and outer lids.

"Open your eyes and look at me if you can," he ordered.

She did so and he could see bits of sand and some larger pieces of debris in her eyes. He asked the woman who had offered to help to sit and let the girl lean back in her arms while he flushed out her eyes. The sand and flecks of material washed out as he released water in the eyes one at a time. Tipping her head, it flowed from her eyes.

When the sand devil knocked her down, she fell on her tote and towel. The rest of her possessions were swished away and were probably somewhere down the beach. Turning to the helpful woman, whose name was Kate, he asked if she could see any clothes in the tote. She ruffled through the bag and said, "No."

What to do? He then went back to his towel and grabbed his jacket and returned to put it on the shivering girl who was still in shock. "My jacket will be a little large but it is a bit more modest and warm. Thanks for brushing all the sand off her body, Kate."

Looking in Deb's tote, he spotted a hair brush. "Can you brush her hair back away from her face so any sand in it will fall away and not get in her eyes while I change the compresses?"

"Of course," she replied. Sitting behind Debby, she brushed an amazing amount of sand from her hair. Her hair must have been wet when she got hot, for this much to be left in it.

They finally got her to her feet. Gary said to Debby, "Close your eyes again and hold this wet towel over your eyes. Kate and I are going to go to the snack-shack to sit and wait until we get all of our gear up there to our cars. You only have what you are wearing plus your beach towel, and your tote. Where is your wallet, your ID, and your phone?"

"They should be in my tote in a side zipper section," Debbie said.

Kate was holding the tote. "I didn't see that compartment when I looked before. Yup—but here is the wallet, the ID, and your phone."

Since she was holding the compress with two hands, she couldn't hold the tote, so Kate set it next to her feet as she sat at the snack shop's counter. When they returned with all the gear the attendant said, "I'll help you with all that stuff. I have a dolly we can put your stuff on, or we can transport you over the wooden path on it."

"I have to get her to the hospital, that big building looming on the hills on the far side of town. There is a large piece of plastic in the left eye and it has to be professionally removed. I'll drive but it would sure help, Kate, if you could come and help to steady her in the back seat."

"Of course, I'm coming. Why did you think otherwise?" Kate slid into the back seat and settled Debbie in her arms.

It took Gary about 20 minutes to reach the hospital. An ambulance would have taken that long to get to them at the beach and even longer to reach the hospital. Gary drove right to the emergency room and an attendant came out with a wheelchair for Debby. Gary had phoned that they were coming in with an emergency and since he was an intern at the hospital, they should hurry.

Kate said, "I had a suspicion you were a man in white, Doc."

"Not yet, but I'm working on it."

Debby was admitted and headed to an operating room in 20 minutes. The eye surgeon had been waiting in the emergency room when they got there. Thirty minutes later he emerged through the swinging doors.

"You did fine, Gary. She had a few minor cuts in the right eye which we treated with an antibiotic ointment, while the left eye is more serious. I extracted the plastic, but it cut deep. You should notify her family that we are holding her over night to make sure the bleeding is not a problem," and he turned and left them.

"Notify her family? I don't even know her last name. Is she local or tourist? I'll have to wait until she's conscious before I can do anything more."

Three hours later the nurse came out of recovery to say he could see her now. She was coherent, and grinned.

He entered and went to the young lady in the hospital gown. When she opened her right eye which was blood shot and purplish from the antibiotic oil she looked into the most beautiful blue eyes she had ever seen.

"Hi, I'm Debbie Blackstone. I don't know how to thank you enough, Doctor. My but you have beautiful eyes."

"And, I return the compliment, Debby, but I'm not a Doctor, just an intern here. Yours are the most beautiful bloodshot eyes I've ever looked into and that left one is going to be just as well," said Doctor Duffy.

And they smiled, eye to eye.

Pooh-Chi, The Happy Dragon

By Betty Wyatt
Submitted on November, 2019

This is a story from the third dynasty of China by a court reporter of a tale from the second dynasty.

Pooh-Chi was a Little Dragon. Not a baby, but a full grown Chi-Fi—the third species of Dragon. In ancient days in China when dragons roamed the skies and land, natives could see Great Dragons, who lived on the north side of the Himalayans and who varied in size from 25 to 50 feet in length.

There were very few of these great beasts, but they are the ones you are probably most familiar with. They are the colorful red and black fire belching monsters we see depicted in murals, in myths, and in all manner of Art.

The second species, Chi-Bat Di, or middle size Dragon, originated on the south face of the Himalayans in India. They are green and brown scaled, with a long red bar extending the back of their large eyes to mid-neck. Whereas the Great Dragon bore only one young every other year, the middle-size dragon bore two every year. They were therefore much more common and crowded in their habitat, necessitating migration for them.

They broke into several sub-species as they spread to Japan, Indo-China, the Arab countries, and now are invading the far Western wild lands. Stories from that savage land tell that the savages built Kassel's (*Chinese spelling of Castle during third dynasty*) to store supplies, and the dragons frequently raided them.

The third species is the Chi-Fi or Little Dragons to be identified as a species. Believing to be the youngest of the other species for many years, they are variable shades of green on their back scales and yellow on their bellies, and vary in length from 6 to 12 feet. They can produce fire as their larger kin can, and they can also ascend higher, since they are lighter and the air bags that lift them are proportionately larger.

Unlike the great 12 blasts of flame from the Great Dragon or the 10 foot torches from the Mid-size, the Little Dragon expels bubbles of flame about 5 feet long and can also expel sparklers of flame up into the air. Unlike his cousins who can only roar, he has the gift of laughter and can hum songs and can dance. Hence his other name, the Happy Dragon. They live in small family groups of five or six, and in the last Dynasty before ours, it was learned that they could be tamed.

The present Khan's daughters each had a Panda, and the Khan's eldest son in the previous dynasty to ours wanted his own pet too. Hence his father thought a Small Dragon would be the perfect gift for a future Khan. So hunters went forth to find an appropriate dragon for the boy.

They found him in central China with his happy family. He could hum, he could laugh, and he could blow fire bubbles and showers of sparkling small embers. He was a lovely shade of green jade, with a bright yellow belly and long white claws. He was perfect, so Khan's men produced a great net and captured him. He was put into a cage on wheels and taken to the Palace. On the way they learned he could also cry and so could his family. They ascended and followed to the Palace and stayed in the area for a long time.

The Khan's son was delighted with his dragon. While the hunters were on the search, a great cage 50 foot high and 40 feet wide was built with wide doors so the cart could enter and various props could be moved in and out for shows.

It might be the son's pet, but his Father was the only Khan in all of China with his own dragon to display and one so talented he could have been a Circus star.

At first the children only played with Pooh-Chi with armed guards in the cage. Then one morning, Ching Do, the son, was in the cage leading Pooh-Cho through his tricks, when the dragon dropped down on all four feet stretched out before the future Khan.

To the boy it seemed to be an invitation to jump on the dragon's back, so he did. The dragon stood up and began to trot around the ring.

The guards rushed forward but Ching waved them off. Twice around the ring in the four-footed run, then Pooh-Chi rose on his back legs. The boy started to slip a bit and stretched his arms and wrapped them about the dragon's neck. By this time the whole court had poured out of the Palace to see their future Khan riding a Dragon. It was a first and they cheered the boy and his mount.

Paintings were made to preserve the memory and a great mural was placed on one Palace Wall. It became a legend in the kingdom and spread throughout China. The boy and his dragon became companions and he rode his magic steed for years even after he ascended the throne.

The dragon lived for many years and the family who had followed the cart came to visit him often. He was happy in his confine, the center of attention, and with a never ending supply of sweet clover. But he began to tire in the routines and when his Boy, now a young man, went to study to become a Khan, the Dragon was lonely. No one else was allowed to ride him, he never had a mate, and one night he just lay down to sleep and never woke up again.

Harvest Moon Memories

By Betty Wyatt
Submitted on November, 2019

Martha came out and sat down on the porch of their lakeside Mountain cabin. She wanted to watch the moon rise once more. Music floated across the lake from the Lodge on the other side where guests were dancing on the deck and inside to the strains of *Shine on Harvest Moon*. Many people came up to the Sierras to watch this heavenly fall phenomenon.

This was where she had met her husband decades ago—the summer she was 18 and was singing with her uncle's band at the Lodge. She remembered singing the lyrics to the old familiar song:

> *"Shine On, Shine on Harvest Moon up in
> the sky. I ain't had No love since January,
> February, June, or July. Snow time ain't
> No time to set outside and spoon, So
> Shine On, Shine on Harvest Moon."*

The band did a couple more choruses with a male singer, just as the moon was peeking over the rim of the Mountains to the East. Below in the wide San Joaquin Valley the crops had been harvested earlier in the year. A couple of days after the corn and grape and cane crop had been finished, a huge mower like machine rolled into the fields, cutting the stalks to the ground and pulling them into trucks to take them to a methane distillery, while they were still full of sap that could be salvaged from the chopped up chunks and converted to methane to assist with the fuel problem connected with climate warming.

This was a trick the farmers had learned and brought to the Valley from Brazil. Now there was nothing left in the fields but stumps and rubble which were being burned. It created a thick red pall and when the moon rose through it, it was magnified by the red glow that turned it to a coppery hue. As it climbed, the smoke thinned and the moon changed gradually to bronze, and then to yellow, and as it emerged from the ground hugging smoke it let off an unbelievable pearlescent white color.

Martha watched as it made this ascent and began its arching apex across the night sky. It was not reflecting in the lake in spangles of white on blue-black surface of the water when another song caught her attention.

How in heavens name had a 21st century band found this song that she had written decades ago for her summers with John. She had shown it to her Uncle and he had orchestrated it for his band and they played it here at the lodge. She had sung occasionally here, but usually Ben, the trombone-player tenor, did it. It had been published through one of her uncle's contacts, but probably never sold more than a dozen copies. She softly sang the second reprise of her song:

Holiday
"You've made this a wonderful Holiday.
Something to hold when you're far away.
All cares and worries have been apart.
We've shared such wonderful moments,
Sweetheart.
Thanks for the wonderful nights divine.
For all the dreams that you leave behind.
No tears of parting, we'll just say, thanks
for the Holiday.

Tears filled her eyes. She and John got engaged at the end of that first summer to the dismay of both sets of parents. She had no ring, just his fraternity pin. She had turned 19 in August, but they knew it meant more and in January when they wed in Reno, his Mother, Step dad, and Uncle Jimmy accepted it and let them move into Grandmother's Cottage, which they had been renting out since her passing.

John continued graduate classes at the State College and she finished at the Community College. It was a brief honey moon though, because John got his draft notice at the end of the month and had to report on the 1st of February.

He reported to Camp Roberts, but it was not yet finished with its updating from National Guard Training Center to full Army combat school, so there was a delay and they held the group at Monterey. Therefore Monterey was overflowing with others in the same plight, so she came home to continue school with daily phone calls and letters linking them.

Half way through boot camp someone checked John's records and discovered 4 years of ROTC in College with the National Guard one summer, so he was sent to Officers Training Camp. Forty-five days later he was commissioned a second lieutenant and he got a ten day leave.

They spent it at the Johnson's Mountain cabin and that was when she wrote the song HOLIDAY. The Lodge was really not open so they had the Lake and Forest for themselves. A couple of days at the end were spent in Modesto with the family.

Then it was off to Fort Bragg for John and more training. Two months of Field Artillery, which was more like anti-aircraft training, according to John, but he had a good group who were really into it and his Captain was a Fraternity Brother. How was that for luck? By now it was coming up to September with a leave of two weeks before shipping out for who knows where—Europe, Coastal Defense, or South Pacific?

The whole Johnson Family decided to spend the Harvest Moon Break at the Johnson Family cabin. That was fine with Martha and John, and they had a two room loft over the big garage that held four cars in winter weather. They made a fateful decision there.

The *No baby decision*, made when they were wed in January, went out the window. Martha wanted a child, and John wanted a family to come home to. So they spent a great deal of time apart from the family. Vivian, his Mother, understood and encouraged the decision they had made.

Since Martha had never had an engagement ring, Vivian decided to give John her mother's single carat Tiffany engagement ring that had just been sitting in a safety deposit box since her mother's passing. He then presented it to Martha the first day of his furlough.

"We're an unusual pair Martha. First we get married and then we get engaged. Do you accept it?" he said, as he slipped the ring onto her finger.

"Oh, yes," she sighed. "I feel much more married now. Can we afford a wedding ring for you now?" she queried.

"No, not yet. I want a big flashy one when I come home from this mess. I'll be a Daddy then—a Family man." And he wrapped her in his arms.

Sitting on the verandah, engulfed in the splendor of the night and memories, she did become pregnant on that first visit here. They had one briefer visit in

January when they had a 48 hour meeting there. It was their anniversary, and she was in her second trimester.

Martha and Vivian had flown to San Francisco to see him at his embarkation point. She would never forget that meeting. She had always worn her hair in a long pageboy, had seldom worn makeup, and had always been slim. Now, however, she had an obvious bulge, short curly hair, lots of makeup, and wore a maternity suit. When he met them in the airport, he first spotted his Mom and came toward her. He then gave Martha a long look and smiled and walked up to her and held her tight.

"Who dat down der, Girl?" he said, patting her bump. It was a game they used to play when they first dated.

"Dat do be your child, Old Man," and his hug lifted her off her feet.

The next day they were sitting at an outdoor café having coffee. They had been conversing but there was now a pause of a minute or two. John was holding his head down, an expression of despair on his face. He was griping his coffee cup with his right hand and nervously turning a wad of tinfoil that had been on their dessert in his fingers.

Martha could not stand it one minute more. "What's wrong? What's wracking your heart and soul to make you so upset? Is it something I said or have done, or not done?" She asked, stretching her hands out to cover his left hand.

He looked up, "Oh God No. It's nothing about you or us. I'm a little sick in my head, I guess. I wish I had someone to talk to about something. I wish your Grand Dad was here."

"Well, he can't get here before you have to get on that airplane, so why don't you try someone in his business? There's a Church across the street. You know all of the men of God are trained to listen and counsel, whether they are ministers, priests, or rectors."

"So speaks the girl who always solves my problems." He stood up, walked to the corner, crossed on the light, walked to the church, mounted the three broad steps, and entered. He walked hesitantly up the broad aisle of the church inside.

A priest was arranging articles on the alter. He turned and watched with hesitation. He spoke, "Is it so hard to walk here? Then I'll help." He turned and walked to the end of the Communion rail, turned it, and met John at the aisle.

"I'm Father Michael, and how can I help you son?" he said, extending his hand. John took it and introduced himself.

"I'm Lieutenant John Johnson and I think I've either lost or am losing my humanity, Father."

"Let's sit down, Lieutenant" and they did. "Now start at the beginning of this problem."

"I'm California born and bred, Father. I grew up in Southern California where there were lots of Japanese. They were all good citizens, hard workers, and very productive. About a quarter of my high school were Japanese. Three of my best friends, fellow baseball players were Japanese—the pitcher, the catcher, and our star batter, who were all close mates. They are all now serving in Europe in that special Nisei group. If I were to hear that George, who is also a fraternity brother from college or Niki were wounded or dead I would mourn deeply.

"Yet since this last campaign, I don't feel that way about the Japs. I have always been happy to defeat them, to capture them, but I always felt a regret for killing God's children. But not now, for it's not the same. I'm happy to blow up a bunker, and I delight when my men come out ahead. I can respect that now for they seem smarter, and better equipped, but I resent it and want to pulverize their whole country."

"John, stop. You haven't lost your sense of humanity. The fact that you are concerned about it is proof of that. When you were in school and played the other team, what was your aim? To win big against them, wasn't it?"

"Yes, Father, but this is different. When I come back to civilian life am I going to be a driven combative man. Can I return to a civilized state? I'm a savage now."

"John, this church is called St. Michael's in the Field. It was built in Pastures, and the city, San Francisco grew toward it. It was damaged in the 1909 earthquake when all of its artwork was destroyed. So when the congregation restored it, they decided to emphasize the Church's role as a shelter from stress and strife. Hence our murals and altar piece with Christ, the Shepherd for the sheep on one side and little children on the other.

"I am going to ask you to pray with me, but I am going to edit you, for your path in life, and I want you to look into my eyes when we say it so I know you understand it. I think you learned it in Sunday school...." And eye to eye the two men prayed.

"The Lord is my Shepherd, I shall not want.
He leads me beside still waters.
He restored my soul.
Though I walk through the Valley of Death.
I shall not fear any evil, for thou are with me.
Thy rods and staff are God's tool and servants
They comfort me."

"John, remember his tools of prayer and his minions—those who serve God in churches and communities. Their service is the sustenance that feeds your soul and humanity, as much as food fuels your body. Now let us say Our Fathers Prayer and you should join your wife who is seated in the last pew."

They prayed together and Father Michael blessed the much relieved captain, who rejoined Martha with a smile. "Yes, it helped greatly and has given me the tools to fight with."

* * *

Two months later she got an express letter message made out to Martha. "Don't name him John, for its bad luck to name him after his family. Name him Jimmy."

No signature, nothing, but it came from an Army hospital. Two days later an Army car pulled up at the Johnson House as she was sitting in her living room window. They paused there briefly and then came up the path to her door. Putting it off as long as she could, she waited for them to ring and she walked slowly to the door.

"Come in please." She beckoned Vivian who was still standing in her front door to come down. She had known for two days what they came to tell her.

Major John Johnson had been killed in Action.

The Many Steps Beyond The First Step

By Betty Wyatt

Submitted on November, 2019

I had written a myriad of checks to good causes in my 60 plus years, but as I hung up the phone I sensed I had just crossed a big line. The State Chairman of a newly formed group had called to say they had word that the White House was contemplating opening the Federal Lands to mining and drilling for oil.

"They can't do that," I told him. "They're protected by the EPA and the Tri-Nation pact between Canada, USA, and Mexico for Migratory Birds."

"You haven't seen the morning news...The Environmental Protection Act has just had a major cut by that puppet that's running it. Even some California refuges may be cut. This desperate push by big oil which is feeling some revenue loss from the electrification of cars is beginning to ripple to other concerns. We Climate Control groups and other Protection Groups are going to have to band together to fight this one. Time is very short to get the word out and get our teams moving.

"Is there any chance?" he continued, "That something can be put together in San Jose in the next couple of weeks?"

My first answer was a big gulp and silence. "That's a very short notice for anything big."

"It doesn't have to be big. Just get some media coverage that the rest of the state can build on. You do realize how serious this is for Climate Control, our concern, and your Environmental focus?"

"Of course I do," I snapped, "And I'll talk to some people in a better position than I am to do it. Maybe we'll have a rally and some significant speakers. Someone will call you, Mr. Soloman, I promise."

"Thank you, Mrs. Porter. I know you're going to be of such a great help." And that was where I hung up.

I sat for a while thinking about the challenge and who was best to take it up. First the president of the San Jose State Alumni Group, that was the Core Group I was part of, and it contained many members in other protective organizations that they could tap.

Gretchen was enthused. "Who can we get to speak who would draw out the crowds to an outdoor rally?" was her first question.

"I don't know, Gretchen. The Mayor would do it but I don't think he's statewide Media, do you?"

"Well, he's sure getting there fast, but let's see. Kamala might do it but she's not really popular with a lot of locals. How about Dianne?"

"Oh, we can't get her. She's really big. Would she do a little thing like this anyway?"

"Want to bet? We need to make this a cross-the-aisle event. Do you know any Republicans? How about a former Governor?"

"Great, as long as he agrees with our stand," I replied at the great idea. "You need to assemble a group of leaders by Saturday, who head groups affected by this and then let's talk it through. Where we could meet?" And we left it there.

I knew Gretchen would get the ball spinning, not leisurely, but just rolling along. She was probably on her closed circuit contact line by now. She had political ambitions and this could be her launch event.

At Saturday's meeting we decided on assembling near the University, where the lots wouldn't all be full and wouldn't require the short walk to the St. James Park opposite the Federal Court House. After all, this was a legal question and would probably end up here in the 9th Circuit anyway.

The top assignment was finding the speakers for the park, since we already had the permit for the Park. I already had commitments from 85 to over 100 members of the SJSA, and most promised to bring their spouses and friends.

The Climate Control and Anti-Air Pollution Groups were rallying members, and an Electric Car organization said to count them in and they would drive their cars to the rally some way.

Artists TO PRESERVE THE EARTH were making placards, and planning a display for St. James Park. We were in business beyond our fondest dreams. My husband was in shock at my organization skills, as he called them. I was really not doing anything but answering the phone and keeping records.

On day 14 we got a major boost. Arnold Schwarzenegger said he would be happy to come to San Jose again if we could arrange a place for him and three companions to stay overnight. The Fairmont was delighted to accommodate them for dinner and Mayor Liccardo was delighted to join them and our event. This was a commitment we had not expected.

Senator Dianne said Yes, but she would be a brief speaker primarily on Climate Control. There is no need to discuss drilling at this time. We should be saving it for the future when the world nation's supply began to run out. A new point of view!

When Kamala Harris's local group learned that Senator Feinstein was coming and would speak briefly on Climate Control, they said Kamala would appear and speak on Preservation of Wild lands and Wildlife briefly and emphasizes California's leadership position in the field. We must keep our State and Federal Lands intact!

As I reported it all to Mr. Soloman, he was amazed, thrilled, and delighted. "Two Senators and one Ex-governor? My, how did you do it?" he asked.

"I didn't do any of it," I replied. "It was individuals with contacts in all these other groups. Contacts, contacts—you can't beat them."

Two days before the event, we learned that a group of several thousand teenagers would be marching from San Jose State to downtown with bands and then marching back to City Hall. Their theme was "DUMP TRUMP!" It's not clear if they wanted to impeach him or defeat him. They have parking lots and City permits for a parade at 10 o'clock. This was panic committee.

Since the City Courts are closed this weekend, the Mayor suggested we contact the Armory for parking and his office will change our parade permit to First Street south to St. James Park and keep our time at 2:00 pm. If we can get the word out in one day we are saved.

Out of town organizers we know about are given the new parking site and parade route. We learned at this time that two busloads are coming from Fremont with handicapped vets and they may parade if they can have banners with *"Vets who fought to save our Country, Now We Parade to save our Planet."* Since we have the electric cars I turned that problem over to that committee and they okayed it.

Social Media helped us big time and individuals reaching out to their contacts were also the key to saving the event. At 1:00 pm Tom and I arrived at the Armory Parking lot. It was already full and I began to worry, but an attendant at the closed Court Parking opened the gate and the mass moved in. When the electric cars arrived, I lost Tom who had to check them out, but he bought me a Green Balloon with a bird on it that one group was selling as a fund raiser for their bird program.

So, armed with my green balloon I went in search of Gretchen at the sign-in booth. Three of the electric cars were being used to transport our ex-Governor and the two Senators, and a fourth was used to carry the Mayor and his wife. A nice touch.

The two buses from Fremont had arrived and it was decided that they would be at the end of the parade. At 2:00 pm on the dot the first red electrified car rolled out slowly to First Street and the march of probably a thousand people followed, carrying the Placards made from the Artists to identify their groups.

The one factor we hadn't factored on was a crowd to watch it. But social media in letting out the news about the change in route did that for us. I'm sure Arnold Schwarzenegger's presence was also a big reason, for many on the sidewalk crowd contained wavers. There were people in every block. It was such a surprise. The closer we got to the Federal Court, the more we had viewers, also carrying sympathetic signs.

An elaborately decorated speaker stand that could hold all the brass and in addition 8 or 10 Large TV screens were set up throughout the park to allow the audience better views and allow them to hear the remarks better. Gretchen and the leaders of several of the local groups were standing on the speakers stand. It was really impressive.

Tom and I had brought stools to sit on but the bulk of the crowd just brought blankets or beach towels. The press and TV news group were much in evidence. Each time one of the electric cars pulled in, there was a cheer from the crowds. The mayor was first, then Senator Feinstein, and she was escorted to the stand, followed 5 or 10 minutes later by Senator Kamala Harris who had made many stops along the route to shake hands with folks who ran out from the crowd to touch her or to wish her well in her campaign.

Arnold was last along with cheers from the sidewalk folks which would have had run out of fans except that two motorcycle cops were escorting Arnold's car. A bulge of about 300 late arriving walkers arrived next and settled on the ground, followed by the Vets' busses which marked the end of the parade. The buses drew a stand up from the seated crowd with cheers and applause. The second bus stopped by the speakers stand before proceeding, and a wheel chair veteran emerged.

In a WW 2 uniform and chest full of medals his attendant similarly garbed, brought him to the edge of the stage. The attendant signaled for a helping hand as three men from the crowd came forward to transport the wheel chair to the platform.

Arnold Schwarzenegger came forward to help and walked with the chair holding the vets' hand till they reached the row of seated speakers.

Gretchen and Mayor Liccardo advanced to the stand. There were flags on the stand and after Gretchen welcomed everyone and introduced the Mayor, he asked everyone to rise and join in the salute to the flags. The Star Spangled Banner was playing through the speakers of the TVs and it was really impressive.

When everyone was seated again, the Mayor spoke briefly about California and San Jose's record of doing the Right Thing and the need for all those in attendance to be aware of threats to "The Right Thing." He then turned and introduced Senator Feinstein, who gave a brief ten minute explanation of the problem they were faced with and why we were all gathered.

It was a brief solid story of saving the resources we have and the planet we live on. She thanked everyone of the many background from coming and she apologized for leaving so soon. "I really wish I could stay longer in this wonderful atmosphere of agreement with citizens willing to be involved."

She blew them kisses and on Liccardo's arm descended the platform to much applause. Her car was at the curb and those on her side took her from Liccardo who returned to the platform. He introduced Mr. Soloman as State Chairman of the Climate Warming Concern committee who briefly covered the back ground of this Rally and the amalgamation of all the groups coming together here in San Jose to carry their messages to Washington. Then he pointed to the several booths set up around the edge where they could sign petitions directly about the problem.

He left the podium and the Mayor again moved up to introduce the five heads of different groups directly involved with the problem if the government opened the Federal Lands to managing and drilling for oil. They spoke as a committee discussing the problem. Arguing, agreeing, and a half hour dramatization of the problem. A well written and directed bit of theater that brought laughs, boos, cheers and heads shaken as the audience realized it was just theater.

"We're going to take a 15 minute break here before introducing our last three boosters. You will note the food trucks have arrived if you feel the need for sustenance. We will be entertaining you by *Sons of Terra*, a newly formed group which may have some familiar faces on it."

A band had been setting up at far stage left and now the drums were moved out onto a rolling platform, five musicians in partial space costumes strolled out, and began to play. It was a strange blend of sound, a little country, a little rock, and then something likely to score as a space film. Folks obviously enjoyed it. They were dancing on the green. Others had run for the food trucks and were now eating take-out food or drinking coffee. As the musicians were ending their stint, the vocalist stepped up and said we will now tell our story.

The band began playing a sweetly sad song:

> *We are the sons of Terra, a planet that has died.*
> *Some folk called it Earth, and it had many names.*
> *But the children didn't try hard enough or soon*
> *Enough, so our Planet died.*
> *And now we live on rocket ships or moons of*
> *Other planets, because our planet died.*

They bowed and left the stage, to applause and their crew cleared the stage. The speakers had been assembled back stage in a sort of green room. Now they all came back.

Gretchen came to the microphone and asked everyone to return to seating. Several hundred of the side walk contingent had walked on down to the park and joined the rally. They were seated around the edges of where the various stakes in the ground designating groups participating were held. Many had signed petitions in the break.

When Mayor Liccardo returned to the microphone and asked for quiet, he said he wanted to bring the attention to another side of the Climate Warming Problem, and he introduced the Wheel chair Veteran, Sgt. Jerome Brown, an Afro-American.

"My message is simple," he said. "Man is not just destroying Earth here at home but Latinos are burning the Amazon to grow soy beans. It is the lungs of the world for clean air. Various Armies are bombing and sterilizing fields that have fed nations for years. There is no longer any place on Terra that you can go and find a vibrant, balanced habitat. I know because I helped with much of the devastation in Vietnam. I pray nightly that God will forgive me for that and we may open our eyes and our minds to what we, all mankind, are doing to this precious home."

And he pushed away from the microphone. There was no applause or cheers after he spoke—just deeply thoughtful silence.

The Mayor returned. "Thank you, Sgt. Brown, for reminding us that we are the shepherds and keepers of this Earth. Our next speaker is one charged by law to see that we do so—Sen. Kamala Harris."

She spoke for perhaps 15 minutes on preserving wild lands and the wild life that depends on them. Then for two minutes she spoke on the need to preserve clean water and clean air for mankind. She left the podium to applause and cheers.

Then the mayor came to the microphone to introduce an old friend of California and their complex problems. Though best known as a superstar of cinema, he is special to use as a former Republican Governor, but one who is wise beyond party lines— Arnold Schwarzenegger.

A wild welcome was given to the familiar figure and the well-known voice. He spoke as a fellow citizen of the Terra, as the band had just proclaimed. He had lived and traveled all over this Globe, the 3rd Planet from the Sun. He loved it and wanted it to survive and he liked the majority of its human inhabitants and thought them worth saving. He was concerned that some members of the party he once lead were remiss in the care they were giving us and our planet. There may not be enough rocket ships to transport all of the billions of living planet so we better get busy in saving the world we've got. And then he sat down.

Cheers probably carried for blocks. Mayor Liccardo and Gretchen came to the microphone Gretchen thanked all of the hundreds of volunteers who made the Walk and Rally possible, including the speakers who gave their time to share their thoughts on the problem. She also thanked The Sons of Terra, and most of all gave thanks to the more than 2,000 who heard her message here today by coming.

The Mayor thanked them for coming. "I hope they all remembered to keep this little corner of the park trash free by using the waste receptacles and will go home to share the messages heard here and share with their family, friends, and community. Have a safe trip home or take a stroll around downtown if you haven't been here for a while. We're growing again."

The sponsoring crews were already striking their booths and gathering displays, although around some booths were members talking, some getting more information. It was around 8 pm before the food trucks had left and St. James Park was back to normal with very little litter, as the garbage trucks appeared to collect the last of the trash.

Now you could catch it on the Evening News and relive it. The coverage was excellent.

When Two Strangers Meet

By Betty Wyatt

Submitted on November, 2019

Carla sat on a bench eating her lunch alone as she did most days. She knew very few of her high school classmates. She was a tall girl, 5'9"s, who had been transferred from Val Verde High School in her sophomore year to Roosevelt High, to bolster the school's soccer team. She was one of only a dozen or so Latino students here at Roosevelt and felt very isolated, but her parents were adamant about her accepting the transfer offer because Roosevelt not only had a great soccer team, but ranked as the top academic school in the district.

She was eating her lunch she had made before leaving home and catching the green bus that ran from the Spanish speaking area of Val Verde into the newer section of the city. As she slowly consumed the pineapple slaw, she was flipping through the school's paper which was hot off the press. She had picked it up from the journalism room just before heading for her bench under the shade tree at the far end of campus.

The lead story was about the coming Senior Prom which was still two months away, but it was the 25th Anniversary of the school, so they were making a big production of it. It would be at the city's top hotel in the ball room with live music, not a DJ with records.

She smiled an ironic smile. She might never be going. Who would ask her? Her height, her Latino heritage, and her schedule of classes as a Home Ec. major all worked against her meeting or knowing any boys.

Oh well, it didn't matter. Her Prom would be next year. She folded the paper and dropped it in her tote. When she looked up, she was startled to see Crusher Cummings, the 6'3" captain of the men's soccer team, standing above her head.

He looked very nervous and squared his shoulders before speaking. "Carla, you don't know me and since we have never met, I don't know you but I have a problem. I'm a senior this year ..."

"I know that Crusher—everyone on campus knows you. You're our big Soccer Star and a sure bet for a college scholarship," she interrupted.

"Nice of you to say that, but I don't know anybody but the guys on the team. That's my problem. I can't meet any girls on my schedule—auto shop, science, chemistry, and math. That doesn't appeal to girls."

Carla laughed, "What a low opinion you have of the female of the species. I have a similar problem. For example, classes in Home ED, Art, Soccer, and a class in Journalism, which is the only class with boys in it, and the tallest one is 5'6" tall. I feel like a hulking beast. Please sit down, my neck is beginning to ache."

She put her lunch into a small container and into the tote, except for a large sandwich which she tore in half, extending the large section to him.

"I made it myself, baked the bread, made the sauce and blended the filler. Let me know what you think."

"Oh my God! You have a sense of humor and you can cook. Look how much I've learned about you already," he said.

The sun broke through the shading branches at that moment and shone upon Carla's face and arms. Her skin literally glowed and he realized for the first time that she was very beautiful. Her hair, which was worn in a boyish cut for soccer, was like black silk and her brown eyes had the longest lashes he had ever seen.

"Carla, will you go to the Senior Prom with me?" he blurted out. "My name is really Kevin Cummings, but most people who know me call me KC. Will you come?"

Carla was clearly shocked and her eyes fluttered her long lashes. She said nothing for several seconds and then with a shy smile said, "I will definitely consider going to the prom with you, but I think we need to get a little better acquainted before I tie you down with a wish and a binding Yes.

"Of course I'll go with you. I'd like you to meet my family and I should like to meet yours to see if they approve of you asking a Latino to such an important event."

"You're right, of course. Let's go to lunch Friday off campus—Arby's, Togo's—you name it. "

"This is a firm Yes, KC. Arby's it is. Where shall we meet?"

"You'll be in Journalism. I'll meet you in front of the building in my red truck. You have made my Mother so happy. She has really been on my case about me going to the prom and lining up my date early. Two months should suit her, don't you think?"

And he went on whistling on his way back into the main campus. Carla gathered up the remnants of lunch, trash to the container just beyond the bench, and the rest in the tote. She was going to the Prom with someone tall enough she would have to look up to him when they danced. What would she wear? Could she and Mother whip up a something special? She could hardly wait to share the news. And they had a date for Friday. He was much more human than she had expected.

Friday's date was a short one, where they ate inside and saw no one who seemed to be students from Roosevelt.

"I know it's very short notice, Kevin, but my folks are anxious to meet you. We could get that out of the way if you are free to come to dinner on Saturday or Sunday night."

KC was holding both her hands at this point and he replied. "Sunday, what time?

"We eat early on Sunday. Is 6:00 too soon? Dad will be home from his Law Office, and Mother likes to go to evening services at St. Viviana's, if that isn't too early for you?"

"Your Dad is a Lawyer? So is mine. See how compatible it's going to be. We're going to be wonderful friends, Carla. By the way, you've never told me your full name yet."

"Carla Anita Tomaso. I have to add a Saints name this year, but we haven't worked that out yet. You probably figured out already that my initials spell CAT. That's my byline on my column in the paper."

"Cats scratch, but they can purr too. I'll just call you kitten."

"Carla will do for the moment, KC. See you at 5:45 pm on Sunday."

* * *

Kevin pulled up in front of an old two-story stucco house, with a beautifully landscaped front. A long staircase led up a slope to a broad veranda and carved double doors. This was a mansion. Ever since he had turned onto the street he had marveled at its traditional upscale houses. He had never thought of Val Verde as having an upscale neighborhood. He had thought of the Latino area as being home to immigrants and borderline citizens. He suddenly realized he was one of those patronizing kids he had scorned.

Had he thought of Carla this way? She obviously wasn't, for this home signified wealth. As he climbed the stairs and rang the bell by the carved door, he was changing his attitude. Carla opened the door and invited him in. She ushered him first to her parents who had come to the hall to meet him—a handsome couple who wore broad smiles of welcome. They then introduced a teenage boy and two younger girls— Peter, Sandra, and Margarita.

They all adjourned to the living room and were seated and making get-acquainted conversation. Carla's father knew Kevin's father and Mrs. Tomaso knew his Mom through school board connections.

Kevin for the first time in his life felt surprised by these friendly, gracious people. He was almost shy. At six on the dot a maid appeared in the opening to the next room to announce that dinner was served. They all rose and entered a beautiful period dining room with crystal chandeliers and a beautifully set table with candles and flowers. The meal went exceedingly well.

Kevin's shyness melted as one luscious dish followed another. Carla, sitting next to him, was drawing him out of his shell, and they were all relaxed and laughing together by meal's end. When they adjourned to the game room, Peter and Kevin fell into deep soccer talk, while Margarita settled to the piano and began playing the piece she would play at next week's recital.

After an hour of family time, Mrs. Tomaso excused herself to go to the special service at St. Viviana's for immigrants. She was on a State Committee working on Latin American domestic problems.

Kevin, remembering his manners, stood as she was leaving. Then he turned to Carla to say, "I guess I should leave too, Carla. Mr. Tomaso, thank you for a wonderful dinner experience. It's been a wonderful evening and meeting your family has been wonderful, Carla. Thank you for inviting me."

Her dad spoke up, "Carla, why don't you take Kevin for a scenic drive of Val Verde and show him all the new improvements. He seems interested in our effort at curing the homeless problem, so show him some of the solutions that are working for us. It's still light outside, so thank you for coming, Kevin."

Carla grabbed a jacket from the hall closet and she and Kevin went down to his Dad's car and toured the very surprising Val Verde Township.

"Why didn't you warn me your families were aristocrats Carla?"

"Are they?" she queried slyly. "They're just Mom and Dad to me."

"Have I been a condescending snob to you, Carla? If so, there is no way I can wipe the slate clean. You are so special to me that if I did so, I'm sorry."

"Kevin, you never were so. You are the first person at our school to seek me out. You took me as just another human being and I appreciated that so much. Granted that I've been surprised you asked me to the prom, but it seemed to be a sincere invite and I loved it. If my family's money intimidates you, forgive them. They inherited their money from two generations back and have made it grow by their own efforts.

"Dinner at our house will be very different, Kitten. Dad is planning to barbecue while the weather is still nice and not too hot. Mother said to bring your swim suit and a towel. We'll take a dip in the pool before dinner. OK?"

"I can hardly wait. I'm looking for a typical Gringo barbeque. What time will you pick me up on Saturday?"

"How about Two pm?"

"Perfect," as they pulled up at the base of the long stairway.

She pulled his face toward her and kissed him on his check.

"You have passed, or he wouldn't have suggested that we tour Val Verde."

She jumped from the car and ran up the stairs.

The meeting with the Cummings went very smoothly because she had no previous misconceptions to wipe away from meeting his parents. She knew about typical American families from TV. But later that night she realized that was KC's source for what he expected in Val Verde. They continued to have lunch together and one Saturday went to the beach where KC spent much time watching the bikini clad girls playing volleyball. She teased him for it and he accepted.

"How else can I get such an anatomy lesson," he quipped.

She wore a one piece swim suit of modest cut which caused a myriad of young and old male heads to check her out when she and KC ran down the beach to plunge into the waves. With water glistening on her skin, as they ran back to their towels, several whistles drew Kevin's scowl.

Meanwhile, in the evening, Carla and her Mother worked on her dress. It was a black crepe sheath with a half skirt in the back that flared out on each side. Three layers of shirred tulle were included so it was very bouffant. But it was also heaving so the layers were stitched onto grosgrain by machine and the grosgrain was hand stitched onto the back bodice. The front of the sheath had broad straps, and was shaped at the bust. She planned to wear her Mother's black pearls with it. The family applauded when she modeled it with black satin flats. She wanted to look as small as possible next to KC.

The night of the Prom, Kevin picked her up and gulped when he saw her coming down the long stair case to meet him at the foot of the hill. It was still light being in late May.

"Oh, my God. You are the most beautiful creature I have ever seen. How will we ever get that skirt into the car door?"

"We planned ahead." She giggled. She saw that her brother had followed her down the stairs and was carrying a long cloth. When she got next to the car, he handed KC one end of the fabric and told him to hold it below her knees. Then he walked around her, crushing the skirt, but not distorting it.

With the skirt now less than door width she could turn and plop into the car seat and they lifted her knees and turned her. The whole family was gathered at the foot of the steps and applauded the safe seating. Shaking his head and laughing, Kevin waved to them all and got into the car to drive away, still shaking his head.

"Girl, I will never understand you. You couldn't just buy a normal dress."

"No, I wanted to show off my design skill. The dress will be the other girls' talk of the ball."

"Well, how do we get you out of the car?"

"I figured how to get me in. You can figure how to get me out," she chuckled.

"We'll keep the wrap around it until we get there and I'll figure something out."

"I never doubted that, Crusher."

"You haven't called me that for a long time."

They pulled into the hotel parking lot, and the valet approached the car, opening the door as he stared. Kevin got out of the car and ran to stand by the valet. Reaching into the interior, he grasped Carla's knees and swung her around as she lifted her knees and feet over the sill. The two men lifted her upright and she stepped away from the car, steadied by the valet. KC handed one end of the wrap to the valet and he walked about her releasing the skirt which she flipped up and out.

The valet laughed and said, "That's a first for me. I hope somebody had a camera, and sure enough a couple did and transferred the shot into his camera and KC's. The keys were transferred and were slip pocketed.

They walked into the Hotel while Carla stopped in front of a large mirror and bent and pulled the inner layer of tulle from its crushed form and had Kevin fluff a couple more spots.

"You are the most amazing girl in the world. I'm so glad that I know you. Are those real pearls?"

"Yes, they are Mother's. Black Pearls from Baja, California."

There was a long line at the head of the ballroom stairs with a dozen couples on the stairs at a time. It took about ten minutes till they started the descent downward and then halfway down, George ("Big Foot") cut in behind them with his date. He pushed her over behind Crusher, and he stood behind Carla where her gown trailed just a bit more each time she stepped down.

George watched it with a devilish grin. Then just before Kevin and Carla were to step off the stairs, he stomped and dragged the tulle back onto his step. His date had been trying to pull him away saying "Stop it George," but Kevin thought he could hear George deviling the girl in some other way, so he ignored it. As Carla stepped forward one and then two steps, there was a tearing sound as the grosgrain ripped from the bodice and the bouffant skirt fell past her waste, revealing her undergarments.

"Wow, look at those pink satin panties," George yelled. And as Carla stumbled forward, Kevin caught her and grabbed the tearing skirt with his right hand to keep it from going further. George's date ran to the left away from George as Kevin turned to George and saw his foot on the black tulle.

"Get your Big Foot off now!"

"Oh, sorry Crusher. Did I impede your progress?" and he laughed as he lifted his foot. Nervous giggles had broken out at the sight of Carla's pink panties. There was a pink neon sign over a door to the right of the stairs and Carla whispered to Kevin, "Take me there."

She was sobbing as they walked with the remnants of the dress trailing them. "Oh, KC, what can I do? I can never go back to Roosevelt. I'll have to go back to Val Verde. I'm so embarrassed. I'm so hurt. I didn't know anybody hated me that much. What's wrong with someone who would do that?"

He held her against his chest and murmured, "No, No, Carla. That's not true, dear. Don't let him win this way. The attendant unlocked the door. She had not been expecting anyone this soon. She saw the disaster and walked out to gather up the skirt while taking Carla from Kevin, and then lead her inside. The band was playing now.

Kevin went back to the edge of the dancing crowd. He spotted George dancing with a redhead and laughing. When he reached the couple he spun the shorter, but bulkier, man around and planted a full force bare knuckle to his chin.

The football lineman was used to blows to his face, so he only staggered. In a moment the two men were rolling on the ground, punching, kicking, and ignoring the rules of legal engagement.

Hotel security men tried breaking it up, but similar fights were breaking out all over the floors with girls screaming. More security appeared and finally the police. Kevin was back on top again and once again leveled one to George's chin, hard enough for him to pass out.

"OK, buddy, you won. Now get up!" the cop said. The arrivals of five cops had quickly quieted down the room. Security was detaining the battlers against the wall. The band which had continued playing through the whole disaster now left the stand.

Hotel management came to the microphone and said, "We have changed the schedule for the evening. We had planned an hour of dancing and then dinner, but we will begin to serve dinner in fifteen minutes in the Gold Room."

Four sets of double doors opened on the wall where security was holding guests to make a statement for the Officers. "Please enter and find your tables as quickly as possible," they said.

Meantime, in the powder room, the attendant had found enough safety pins to get the grosgrain back on the torn bodice. Carla's one girl friend had heard what happened and joined her in the powder room. Others were trying to enter to use the facility, but she sent them to the other room in the area. Carla had stopped sobbing, but washed her face and was sitting on one of the benches.

"Where's Kevin?" she asked.

"The last time I saw him, he was talking to a cop," her friend said.

"Why are the cops here?"

"Didn't you hear? There was a great brawl all over the room when Kevin and George got into it."

"Oh, no, no. All I heard was some girls squealing and the Band playing."

"They were not squealing; they were screaming."

"It's too much. It's just too much. Is there a back way out of here?"

Then, she just left.

Five Chapters
Creative Story

How Green Was That Probe?
Chapter One
Submitted by Betty Wyatt

Ronnie knew he had no business in the lab when Professor Simmons wasn't there, but he had just come in to pick up his lab clothes to take home to launder. They weren't really dirty because the lab was super clean, but they looked limp and tired beside his mentor's crisp garb, which was fresh every single day.

The Professor had not been in for three days and was in the hospital for a check up on the new Laguna—39 Virus that was sweeping the world. It was nothing to panic about yet, but the University had ordered the testing of all staff members anyway.

The virus was completely unknown. It was in the form of a lighter-than-air sphere, slightly smaller than a soccer ball. When the ball burst, it released hundreds of smaller spheres, each containing a toxic gas that would spread about 100 feet. Stanford was studying the balls thinking the virus might be related to the Covid—19 Virus of twenty years ago.

Ronnie, having a set of keys to the inner rooms, was tempted to go into the core of the suite. He went in and flipped on the lights and powered up the sensor. This Lab was not involved in any virus work—rather the technicians were doing deep space research.

Dr. Simmons was working on a completely new track. He had probes of an unbelievable sensitivity, both auditory and visual, that had Ronnie in total awe of his mentor. He could not believe how lucky he felt every day when he came to the lab and sat in the console with earphones and special goggles to protect his eyes from the rays they were using in the probes.

They were not located on the campus, but were up on the Communication Hill where the giant scopes were.

He turned on the search levers for visual, and then he brought up an image of the section near Mars that they had been studying. He then flipped a switch on the right of the screen randomly. The image on the screen began to gyrate and spin. He cried out to no one in particular. "Whoa! That's not normal."

The screen blacked out for possibly 30 seconds and then slowly an image began to form on the monitor. When the image had begun its whirly-gig spinning, Ronnie had risen from his seat ready to dash and turn off all the power switches. Now, as an image was slowly filling the screen, he stood transfixed, watching it grow in detail.

The image showed a large conference room office with many dark-skilled men in green uniforms with insignia on their sleeves, much like our US Navy's uniforms, but the image on the screen was too small to decipher them. The strange thing was that the room and all of the equipment in it were green. Even the light from overhead that looked like our fluorescent tube lighting was colored green.

Ronnie couldn't get an auditory burst on visual and the camera that was transmitting it seemed to be circulating about the ceiling, from the angle of the images. Leaving all the instruments and power on to keep the image transmitting, he walked back into the office and headed for a phone. He called the Simmons home phone and Dr. Simmons' wife answered, after two rings.

"Mrs. Simmons is the Professor coming home soon, or is he still ill?"

"Ronnie, he's not sick at all. He is just being tested for this new virus that is sweeping us and the Orient. I thought you knew that!"

"I did, but I thought something might have turned up. Could you call him and convince him to come home tonight and rush here to the lab? Something he needs to see has just happened! It's really urgent and I don't know how long the image will last. I don't know how to record it because we've never gotten this far. Please, Mrs. Simmons, could you call him and send him to the lab right way. I'll wait for him here."

"I'll try, Ronnie. Our Son, Robert, the lawyer, has been keeping me company. I'll send him to fetch Gordon from the hospital."

"Great, I'm up here at the lab. The gate at the bottom of the hill should still be open, because there's a crew working on the antennas."

In half an hour the phone rang. It was Robert. "We're on our way. Dad was still up and dressed and was playing cards with some fellow virus testers."

Ronnie called Security to make sure the gates would be open at the base of the hill. Since they were coming from the nearby Stanford Hospital, it was just a matter of minutes before he saw the car's headlights. They stopped and everyone literally piled out of the car. Dr. Simmons was running and yelling.

"What the hell happened, Ronnie? What did you do?"

"I'm not sure, Doc, but I think the visual is still working. Quick, let's get to the lab. I don't know how long it will last."

The two rushed into the lab where the visual was still on and the camera was transmitting as before.

"What the hell is that? Did you scan into some stage set where they are filming science fiction?"

That had never occurred to Ronnie.

"If you'll check the coordinates, Sir, you will see that we are on the unnamed channel, as far as I know, Moon or Mars. I knew you would want to know at once since it's your setting, but it was quite a trip for me."

The rest of the group had just come into the inner Lab. Mrs. Simmons, Robert, and the Security Man from the Gate House, and three of the Professor's recent companions. They had all been expecting a disaster, but instead it was a triumph.

"It looks military, Dad," Robert opinioned.

"I think we can all agree on that. But who's who and where? Will it take us a while to find out," his father replied.

Each of the new comers grabbed their phone and they were beginning to transmit.

"Hold it!" Professor Simmons ordered. "Ronnie, get their phones—yours too, Robert. We have to verify what we have found here first."

One of the scientists, Doctor Jim Chargin, a member of the Mars Project, started to argue. "Simmons, I'm not calling social media—I'm calling the Mars Project. They'll have to get on this right away. They will need to fly in a crew who can work with you. This is BIG, man!"

"Ok, Ronnie, hand him his phone and make sure that's only who he calls."

Everyone in the room could hear the answer shouted from the receiver. "Man, what have you been drinking?"

Chargin replies, "I'm cold sober, but in a state of shock over the immensity of what Doctor Simmons has done. You've got to see it to believe it. We have only an image so far, but the lab is set up for sound also. We will need someone who has been studying interspace languages, if there is anyone."

Ronnie reached out his hand for the phone, but Chargin says, "Wait a minute. I did not give him a location yet."

"Dr. Simmons says NO. No one will give such information until we have a full security set up and that means no one can have one to one communication or any contact with social media, friends, relatives—you know the drill, guys. This is a small vulnerable lab and we've got to protect it."

Juan Fujimoto, NASA's Japanese Latino coordinator with Stanford University, docilely asked "Can I call NASA Headquarters?"

"Yes, Juan," said Simmons and turning to Robert he said, "But with the same restrictions."

Walt Adams, the other virus tested card player asked, "Doctor Simmons, we've got to let the University know. They have to be prepared for a deluge of press, TV, radio, and reporters and we need to have a plan. If we don't, this could be a disaster for our departments to have. It's the greatest boon for this project in this century."

"I can see that's true. From your position you can make one call to the President of the University!" Doctor Simmons said.

He then turned to George, the Security Man. "George, get back on that gate and don't let anyone up here, because the gate will be locked. We will need all hands on ground security immediately. No one must go up or down on Communication Hill, not even a peripheral patrol with a dog team, if there is one."

The leak was out. Incoming phone messages were already coming in. The initial call was from the first responders, asking the nature of the disaster. PR Walt

Adams took the call and identified himself on the phone. He spoke to the first responders.

"Boys, I don't know why you are calling. It makes me feel very secure. What made you think there is a problem. There is no problem here. So hold your horses and settle back. There is no disaster—there is no problem, all is okay." And he hung up.

The next call was from the tester program for the Laguna—39 Virus. They wanted to know where Doctor Simmons, Jim Chargin, Walt Adams, and Juan Fujimoto were. The next call was from George.

"Doctor Simmons, I just got a call from Doctor Abelard. He has called out the Army, and an active duty unit, complete with tanks, is on its way to the campus now."

"Oh, hell! I know he's the chief for the security of the campus. But couldn't he check with us first? Tanks on the highway cannot be kept secret. How much information does Abelard have, George?" Dr. Simmons asked.

"So far, information only from hacking your lines, Doc," George answered.

Doctor Simmons turned to Robert. "Rob, you're an attorney. How can we call a halt to this until we know what it is? At this point everything is a problem. We have a lot of green men doing something with gasses unique to Mars and we don't know what they're doing. Even if we turn on the sound and start searching for common formulas, we cannot understand them in all probability."

"Dad, I think this is too big to attempt to keep the word from getting out. This is an Earth-wide important discovery you have made. Turn on the sound, for there's a chance that they may have had radio contact with earth and learned enough words for us to break down what their plans are. We don't even know if what they are doing is aimed at some other colony on Mars, or whether Earth is their target."

A long period of discussion followed. It had never occurred to any of the others in the room that Earth might not be the focus of whatever was going on in the green room—and there could be more life around Mars.

They decided to throw the switch and start searching for any verbal situation from the moon. Silence fell in the room as they searched, and ten minutes later there was an explosion at the transformer on the power line to the antennas on the top of the hill.

Three men burst into the room and the leader of the exploratory sound probe of space was furious. "You killed our power! Six months of work went down the drain! We controlled ten satellites and now we've lost contact with almost all of them!"

Meanwhile, with the computer still running, the sound probe for the Green room had been vibrating furiously and it suddenly made a sound, and the image on the visual was a clearer picture with more detail. A cheer went up from everybody there. Chargin poked the arm of one of the new arrivals, and said, "I think we just trumped your ace, old man."

The now crowded room watched the big screen with fascination. The sound was not so good. It was statically and variable in general, but with the enlarged image, you could tell which person was speaking. A door at the back of the Green room opened a few minutes into the screening, sending a white light into the room, which startled the earthly watchers.

The beam of light shone on a strip of technicians at their machines in the Green room, and they were not brown skinned as supposed but rather were a very ruddy skin color that was turned brown by the green light. This was a very surprising discovery and sent a low wave of comment through the Stanford watchers.

The door then slammed shut but no one had come through it. Those close to the screen could see a small robot-like box had rolled into the room and was headed to a row of raised seats that seemed to hold more important technicians. The box disappeared behind the elevated row. The tech at the end of the row, where it disappeared, lifted it onto the table top where the five men were seated. He opened it and appeared to be describing the contents to the group. They seemed pleased by the report. The center man then launched into an angry statement in the middle of which were the words, *"deadened and quicker."*

Even though the earthlings could not understand the recording tapes for the most part, those two words jumped out at most of them. The group recording the sound transmission played it back to be sure they had a complete copy. What a breakthrough if they had two words of English. Maybe there were other pieces of language caught in bits. They had to copy the sound recordings and get them to linguists who could perhaps pick words in German or in other language so they would form some theory as to what the Green Room was up to.

The team of linguists studying the recorded tapes found dozens of earth language sounds on the sound tape, including the sound for *"dozen"* and *"Afrique"*. These then became very significant.

Four weeks later remnants of one of the balls was found in Libya and within a week, cases of the Laguna—39 Virus were detected, where it had never been seen before. In the week that followed, cases erupted due south of Libya through the heart of Africa.

They could not have picked a more vulnerable area. Europe, the center of the foreign aid group, was so deeply involved in fighting the virus and trying to protect their own populations, that they might not be able to assemble the health teams that they normally sent to Africa to battle medical tragedies.

The Arab North and South Africa are the only areas of that big continent that really have hospitals, clinics, and the medical technicians required to battle another Pandemic. Tests are being run throughout Europe and North America on the old Covid—19 Virus that swept the world back in 2019 to see if it can be modified or updated to fight the new Virus.

So far, no lab has been able to establish a similarity between the two diseases. Tests to date show nothing to relate them, except that those who survive either seem to have immunity for some period afterward.

It was more than five years ago when a vaccine for Covid—19 Virus was eventually found to control it. The Laguna—39 Virus has moved slower and the death rate so far has been around 5% of those detected. The symptoms were obvious also—flushed complexions, nose bleeds, and fever—very different from the Covid—19 Virus.

To date it has broken out in India and spread into Indonesia and the South Pacific Islands. It is slowly moving to North Africa, the Caribbean, and the Gulf of Mexico, into Mexico and Venezuela. Strick lock-downs or social distancing do not seem to affect it. These two pandemics are not the same disease.

Dr. Simmons called his son, "Robert, take them out and give them a seat assignment to the plan how NASA and the Mars Project can transition to take over, if that's the way they want it to go."

The group exited the room, leaving Simmons, Fujimoto, Adams, and Chargin staring into the monitor. Robert had been handling incoming calls, and as the group was exiting the inner lab, the outside phone rang, and he caught it. It was one of the first responders.

"Do you have an explosion on site, and do you need help?"

Robert asked, "How could you know that so soon?"

The voice on the other line explained. "We have fire-watching drones and you have a grass fire."

Robert said, "Ok, but treat it as a routine matter of a transformer overloading and starting a grass fire. Notify PG&E to come fix the transformer and replace any burned lines. I will contact the gate to let you in."

Robert called the gate to admit the first responders in to fight the fire and PG&E to repair the transformer, but he told the first responder that no phones were to be allowed on the site.

Doctor Simmons had been huddled at a table with Walt Adams and Jim Chargin from the Mars Project and Juan Fujimoto from NASA. They were completely connected to the discovery, and he asked Adams,

"Walt, you are an experienced reporter and PR manager. Can you work with Mr. Chargin and Mr. Fujimoto to set up the conference with the agents coming in from their respective headquarters?

"I will try to have a summary report ready for you by tomorrow, and the conference should meet either tomorrow afternoon or the following day, depending on how fast their agents can get here. I know you are familiar with enforcing security restrictions."

As he rose from the table, Dr. Simmons asked the three men if this was agreeable with them, and they accepted it.

Walt Adams said, "Of course, Dr. Simmons, I would be honored to be involved with this story in any way, if I can help you. Ronnie and Dr. Simmons will be available to this new committee by appointment as well."

It was now necessary to clear the inner lab so that Simmons and Ronnie could do some work to advance the study. Dr. Simmons had put his son Robert in charge of the outer Lab. The three men from the satellite were given computers and desks to contact the necessary people in order to get control again of the satellites. In the meantime they would contact the owners of the satellites and discuss the problem with them, but they were to make no reference to the Moon matters.

All incoming calls would go through Robert. As he had been instructed by Simmons, George had contacted Dr. Abelard, Chief of University Security who had brought in the Army which was now dribbling in—the first two tanks and their crews were on the hill and two trucks had arrived with tents, with workers to set them up and equip them.

As far as they knew, they were here because of the satellite problem and the rumor that it had been a Terror attack and that intelligence was working on it. Some of the satellites were apparently Defense and Security projects.

Meanwhile, a Colonel had arrived from Security to inform all occupants of the Lab that they would be guests of the University for tonight and would be transported down the hill by bus and served dinner at the Guest Lodge. Grumbling was heard in both Labs, but the Colonel said alternate accommodations were available at military headquarters in the brig, but the stay there might be longer.

Ronnie again distributed phones and monitored the calls with Robert's help. The Colonel added, "As soon as the mess is set up in the bivouac you will be served a hot meal—probably hamburgers and coffee. With that, the grumbling subsided.

Meanwhile at the inner lab, Dr. Simmons and Ronnie were checking all of their settings and making sure things were OK so they could put the units into a sleep-mode when the time comes. They dimmed the unit and brought it back up. Just before the screen went gray, however, Ronnie shouted, "Doc, that man who just entered from the left side of the green room. It's Gordon Scott. I'll swear it's him."

"Yes, it's definitely him."

Doc shook his head—he was fatigued from the day. "Who is Gordon Scott? The name is familiar, but I can't remember him."

"He's a vanished Astronaut. Remember, he and a civilian on a special mission were flying a near space high altitude mission when they both vanished. They were flying at 50,000 feet right at the edge of space and then they disappeared. They just vanished. There never was any wreckage. No nothing."

Ronnie had run to his recording set up and turned on the display screen to see if he had captured Scott's image before the unit shut down.

"There he is, Doc. What's he doing on that Mars moon?"

Simmons was grinning ear to ear. "There's our key to communication in the future!"

How Green Was That Probe?
Chapter Two
Submitted by Chuck Northup

Suddenly the office door flew open, and a man dressed in full fire regalia rushed in shouting. "You've all got to get out! The fire is headed your way and you may be trapped if you don't get out!"

Simmons faced him and said, "Don't worry, the building is fireproof."

The fireman replied. "The building may be fireproof, but you aren't. The fire will get so hot you'll be cooked like an oven. SO, GET OUT!"

They decided to heed the advice of the fireman and put the console to sleep as previously planned. Everyone rushed off the property to a safe distance and watched as the State Fire Control Unit fought the blaze. Helicopters were bringing loads of water from a nearby reservoir and dumping it on the flames. There were several buildings in the line of fire, and the aircraft was being directed to aim their water on these targets.

Fortunately, in past years, most of the utilities had been put underground so they were safe. Only transformers and antennas were above ground, and since they were metal, they did not burn. The fire was under control quickly, and everyone returned soon to the office.

The rooms were badly overheated, but they were not burned. "We were right to get out. We would have been baked alive if we had stayed," said Robbins. "Let's see if our equipment is still OK." They woke up the console to discover that all was still well.

Dr. Simmons arranged a Zoom conference with conference members. There were attendees from most of the affected countries. The problem to have scientists mixed with political figures was discussed, and it was decided that at this juncture it would be best to have scientists only to produce factual statements.

Experience from the past Covid—19 Virus pandemic provided the lesson that without factual information and full knowledge of the virus' properties, rumor and political show-offs would endanger any progress.

At the Zoom discovery conference, there were over thirty attendees. Dr. Simmons was selected to be the host. He told the conference, "We have called this gathering of knowledgeable scientists to obtain factual information about the Laguna—39 Virus. I would like to call upon Dr. Huang where the virus was first discovered. Dr. Huang is in Ulaanbaatar, Mongolia. Dr. Huang heads the Department of molecular

Virology at the International University of Ulaanbaatar. Dr. Huang, please begin?"

Speaking through a translator, Dr. Huang introduced himself by saying, "Thank you Dr. Simmons. I live in a large city, the Capital of Mongolia, which has a pleasant enough climate, but close by is the Gobi Desert, which does not. Climate makes a big difference causing the Laguna—39 Virus to react differently.

"The travel conveyance of the virus is a sphere, a bit smaller than a soccer ball. By itself, it does nothing but convey the virus to various places. Being lighter-than-air, it floats easily through space, as well as the atmosphere, never truly settling until it reaches an air climate of over 40.5^0 C, or 105^0 F, at which time it bursts, releasing hundreds of microscopic spheres contain the gas Laguna—39, and each gaseous sphere is about the size of a small marble. These are also lighter-than-air and float aimlessly until they strike something and release their toxic cargos."

At this point, many hands went up by those who wished to ask questions. Dr. Simmons called on Dr. Mawasaki, a scientist from Japan.

The Doctor, who spoke perfect English, said, "Our country of Japan seldom reaches temperatures that high. Would the virus still be a danger to us?"

Dr. Huang replied with more of a statement than a question. "Ah, so, but you have volcanos, don't you?

If one of the carrier balls floats over the hot air rising from a volcano, the sphere will probably burst."

Several hands went down when they heard the answer, but other hands still showed. Dr. Simmons called upon Professor Gilbert from London, England.

"The UK has no active volcanoes, even though some of our territories in the Caribbean do. Would our steel manufacturing plants emit enough heat to burst one of those bubbles?"

Dr. Huang conjectured. "The combined heat from several stacks would probably equal a triggering temperature over your large steel manufacturing cities. I would say you are NOT out of danger."

The rest of the hands disappeared, so Dr. Simmons called upon Dr. Bushnell from Texas. "I now want to ask Dr. Bushnell from Texas A&M who has done the most research on the Laguna—39 Virus to speak. Dr. Bushnell?"

"Thank you, Dr. Simmons. At Texas A&M we have an entire cadre of biologists and chemists studying this dreadful virus to determine its properties. It is a very mysterious gas. We are unable to find its ingredients in the Period Table of Elements. This would indicate that it comes from somewhere in space, but we know not where.

"The gas is enclosed in a small sphere that breaks upon contact with a harder object. Since it is very fragile, the hardness of the colliding object hardly matters. It could break upon striking a leaf or blade of grass. The properties of the gas are interesting, however. If it is breathed by man or animal, that person becomes a victim and usually dies within a few days. It requires only one small sphere to kill. If, however, the sphere simply strikes and releases its gas, which is also a permanent dye, then anything it hits will turn green—permanently.

"Since the gas particles are microscopic, they can spread greatly to cover an object. Two particles could easily cover a man, and several particles could paint an entire house."

"We have found that when the carrier ball bursts, the smaller spheres travel about 100 yards, but their green poison dye will spread as a fog envelopes a city. One positive note is that once the dye contacts an object, it becomes harmless. An animal can even lick the area and be safe.

"A further comment—we are furiously working to find both a cure and an immunization against this virus, but we are yet to be successful, mainly because we don't know what element or elements we are fighting."

Again, several hands went up for questions. Dr. Simmons called upon Dr. Salvador from Venezuela. "Dr. Salvador?"

Speaking in fair English, he asked, "Venezuela is a Tropical country. Is the virus more 'active' in higher heats than in Temperate Zones?"

Dr. Bushnell smiled as he said, "That is a super-interesting question. We have spent considerable laboratory time on that very subject. The simple answer is 'YES.' It becomes very complex when you delve further into the question, however.

"We have measured the speed of the spread by millimeters per second in various temperatures, but we have also done the same with various textures. The colder the surface, the slower it spreads. We found that the smoother the texture, the faster the spread is. There are innumerable variables here."

Dr. Ridan from Indonesia then asked, "Does a far-spreading dye get lighter?"

Dr. Bushnell answered, "It depends. The eye is subjective. On a textured object it may seem darker because the texture contains miniscule shadows, but on a smooth surface, yes, it gets lighter the farther it spreads. It is not a paint that maintains its darkness no matter how thin you spread it. In addition, the color will depend upon the color of the object, so the thinner it spreads the more the object color will come through."

Dr. Sanchez from Mexico was next called upon. "Dr. Bushnell, have you found ways to destroy this virus?"

Bushnell answered, "Once it has entered the body, we have found no way to kill it or even control it. Before it reaches the body, however, it can be destroyed by fire or any form of excessive heat. We also found that simple, plain water—even sea water— destroys it, so if a ball drops into the ocean or any lake or river, it will be destroyed. More importantly we found that spraying a mist will kill it. That may be our best way to control this serious threat."

Dr. Bushnell then asked with a peculiar appearance to his face, surrounded by grey hair and a bald top. "You speak of these qualities of this virus, but you say little about its origin or how it got here. Would you care to speak on this part of the puzzle, please?"

Dr. Bushnell's hand came to his chin and his index finger wrapped around his lips as he assumed a position of thoughtfulness. His eye brows dropped into a frown, and he began to speak. "We at Texas A&M have wondered about this aspect a lot. We studied the composition of the outer ball to try to understand what type of atmosphere it came through, besides our own here on Earth.

"The outer shell is strong enough to withstand the entry into our atmosphere, and obviously we can withstand the stress of outer space without bursting. We don't know what this material is. It could have come from a great distance, having floated until reaching Earth. Our feelings are that it travels on light waves. We also feel that since we have discovered more than one, it may have been aimed at Earth. The only place we have discovered so far that might sustain life, as we know it, is Mars."

"Excuse me, Dr. Bushnell," interrupted Dr. Simmons. "The central reason for assembling this conference was to discuss the recent discovery of life on one of the moons of Mars. It seems quite likely that this virus ball came from that source. I would like to open up our discussion to this subject now that we know something about the composition of the virus. I see many hands going up at this time. I'll start with you Dr. Fujimoto, since you were present at this discovery. Dr. Fujimoto?"

"I was not exactly present at its discovery, but immediately thereafter. What our space console accidentally picked up was a scene in a laboratory on a Mars moon. The beings were human-like with darkened skin, but it was difficult to determine their color because the entire laboratory was green, like the dye which was described earlier.

"The laboratory seemed similar to those we use, but it was a more advanced style. In order for the transmission of images, there had to have been a camera floating about in the lab with artificial intelligence guiding it. The beings used a robot which entered the room as we watched. The beings also spoke a language we didn't understand, except for a few English words which came through the transmission. We did not understand how they could use English until a human appeared. That man was our missing astronaut, Gordon Scott."

At the mention of that name, nearly everyone on the Zoom conference uttered an astonished sound.

Dr. Fujimoto continued. "We must assume from this that Scott survived the crashing of our unsuccessful exploratory rocket that NASA sent up last year. So far, we have no way of knowing if others survived."

The next questioner asked Dr. Fujimoto, "If that laboratory is all green, does that mean the virus is everywhere in that location?"

Dr. Fujimoto threw up his hands saying, "More assumptions. We have few facts. We have seen only the interior of one lab and its inhabitants. We do not know what exists outside that small area. All of the beings and Gordon Scott were completely green. All of the surroundings were green, including anything we could see. We have to assume from this that it is caused by the virus and that the beings are immune to it. If Scott is living a normal life, as it seems that he is, they must have immunized him against the virus. That idea alone gives us hope that there is an immunization available, if we can only discover it."

More questions were fired at Dr. Fujimoto. "Since you are the NASA Coordinator, I question whether the Mars beings are attacking us, or is Scott sending us samples to experiment with. I wonder if Scott is being held prisoner and are they attempting to fish information from his brain."

Fujimoto resumed, "Scott could be a prisoner, as you suggest, or he may not be. We don't know. It is obvious that Scott has gotten them to speak a few words in English, so he may be able to understand them to a degree. We feel that Scott will be our source of correspondence with Mars."

Another question came forth. "If Scott is walking around the lab with others, then that must mean that the gravity is similar to that on Earth. Otherwise he would be much lighter and would be walking in a floating fashion. Are you sure that the location is only a moon of Mars, or is it on Mars itself?

Fujimoto answered. "The moons of Mars are of different sizes and travel at different speeds around Mars. When we captured this scene from what seemed to be a moon, it may really have been a moon passing by a spot on Mars, and our console actually picked up a location on Mars behind the moon.

"If that is the case, we would be looking at the back side of Mars, and Scott could be walking rather normally. We don't know the weight of the other beings.

We do know that from the appearance of their clothing, it seems they are wearing uniforms like military police, so these beings are not just citizens. We also do not know if any form of gender is involved. We can presume that they are capable of reproducing themselves, and that their forms are similar to human. We also know that their complexion is ruddy, which turns brown under green light, so therefore, the beings are not themselves green."

Dr. Simmons finalized. "Since we have no further questions from this conference, I've selected Dr. Jim Chargin to assemble a group to summarize this meeting's findings and publish them to the public. We all will be able to start out on the same footing. We still have few facts, but this conference has stabilized the rumors that may float about and keep further conjectures under some control. With that I close this Zoom conference."

Back in his own lab, Dr. Simmons assembled the recordings of their Martian visit so he could send copies to those who desired one. He knew this would cause much discussion and conjecture about life on Mars. Up until now, we could never see the back side of Mars, for we didn't know if any life existed there. We do know that the side we do see is very desert-like, devoid of water, as far as we know, so perhaps Mars inhabitants need water and look upon Earth as a good source. They could even be considering taking over our planet. That might be the reason for sending the Laguna—39 Virus to Earth in order to destroy its inhabitants. That term, *deadened and quicker,* might be a clue to our destruction. Sending that virus could certainly deaden us more quickly. If that's the case, their desire for water may also be their downfall because the Laguna—39 Virus is destroyed by water, and Earth is 71% water. We on Earth also have the capability of using water from pipes to destroy this enemy. That leaves only 20% of Earth for the virus to land on without destroying itself.

The distribution of the virus ball discovered so far indicates that there is no particular target on Earth for this attack. For all we know, many balls may have landed in water and been destroyed. The only ones we have not discovered have been in more arid places or drifted from arid places. The latest one found in Libya would be of greater danger because of its closeness to the Mediterranean Sea and to Europe.

He pondered—the prevailing winds over Libya in North Africa are from west to east. Few air currents travel northward, and none go westward, so there is little danger of the Laguna—39 Virus traveling from Libya to Europe or to western Africa.

"The Mediterranean and the Atlantic would probably protect the Americas and Europe, but countries east of Libya would still be in danger. We must notify those countries immediately. That area of the world is somewhat dry and does not have a great abundance of water to use for protection. We may have to supply water bombers that we use for forest fires so they can obtain more water. We should be able to equip our bombers with misters for that particular purpose.

"The spread of the Laguna—39 Virus to the Caribbean and countries surrounding it is another story. The virus ball evidently landed in the western area of Mexico and spread eastward to the northern countries of South America.

"By the same token, the spread of the Laguna—39 Virus into the islands of the South Pacific and Indonesia indicate it was another virus ball that caused those occurrences. Winds in those areas are affected by the monsoon seasons and can be in almost any direction. In addition, the islands are surrounded by water, so the virus cannot spread too far except by accident. I don't think the main lands to the north or south will be in danger from that source.

"And thinking of Gordon Scott, he is probably trapped on Mars. His rocket is probably in no shape to return to Earth. We don't even know if the other astronauts are still alive or what condition they are in. Can the Martians build a rocket capable of flying to Earth? They seem advanced in some areas such as flying a camera and controlling the virus among their own inhabitants. Scott didn't die from the virus so they have some immunization, maybe even a cure. But they lack water as far as we can see. Scott is still alive, and he needs water to live, so they must have some means to create water.

"I wonder if Scott is being forced to work for them so they can pick his brain. He has no means of escape so perhaps he's going to become one of them. He wouldn't be the first slave to become a turncoat. He will learn about them and perhaps will be able to help us in this way with communication.

"The Martians may not know we are watching them. The radio signal they are using may be one that simply goes out in all directions, so they are unaware. If we can get a signal to Scott, we may be able to set up a link to exchange information. That would be more valuable than our exploratory rocket and landers. We have had several landings on Mars, but the results have been disappointing because of finding no signs of life. Without knowing what's on the other side of Mars, however, makes this breakthrough more valuable and interesting.

"The side we see is only desert. If there is life on the other side, and their explorations could not survive very far in that environment. Or perhaps they have explored and found that since there's nothing there they can use, they have simply left it alone.

"He muttered to himself. It's been a long day. I think I'll go home." He closed up the lab, got into his car, and drove the few miles to his home off campus.

How Green Was That Probe?
Chapter Three
Submitted by Tom Brandt

Dr. Simmons sat in his car for quite a few minutes before he approached his front door, as he tried to untangle the contradictions from the last conversation. He greeted his wife who gave him a warm welcome.

"You look weary," she said.

"I am. I need a spot of sherry."

He dropped his briefcase in the visitor's chair in his small home office and returned to the kitchen where his wife had the sherry decanter and the glasses laid out on the breakfast table. He poured one for each of them when the doorbell intervened.

She went to answer it and soon Dr. Simmons heard her voice. "Robert, how good of you to come. Your Dad needs someone to ventilate with."

"I thought I saw that far away glaze in his eyes as we left. Is he around?"

"Yes. He's in the kitchen. He's just poured two Sherries. I hope you're in the mood. I need to go to bed."

Dr. Simmons rose as his son entered the kitchen.

"Dad, for heaven's sake, please sit down. I see you've got your good sherry out. You must have a lot on your mind."

"I do. I'm very disappointed with my colleagues. I've not heard such a recitation of half-truths and folklore from people who should know better. They even got me sucked into the swamp when I agreed that there are no winds blowing from east to west in this hemisphere. The Trade Winds do exactly that— blow from the Canary Islands to the Grenadines. I don't know what got into me."

Robert pushed one glass of Sherry toward his father. "Let's drink to one good mystery."

After they had savored one or two generous sips, Robert said, "What's troubling you, Dad."

"That performance left me cold. I used the word "performance" because that's what it felt like."

"In some respects, I must agree with you. Gordon is an air-breathing critter, so where did they get the oxygen?"

Robert paused for a swallow of Sherry. "They can't run a concentrator because there's nothing to concentrate. He walked a bit strangely, too. It looked to me like he hasn't totally adapted to the one-third gravity."

Dr. Simmons grunted. "Dammit, there's another thing. Those creatures looked too much like us. We humans evolved in a lush environment, with a wide variety of flora and fauna. The first of the great apes stood upright about three million years ago. It took nearly all that time from then to get where we are now. I need convincing about their background."

"So, you don't buy that they are locals?"

"No, not for one second I don't."

"That will disappoint some of those folks."

Robert shook his head in disbelief and then excused himself to get a pitcher of water and to make a brief pit stop. As he returned, Dr. Simmons said, "Good idea!" and left on a similar errand.

"Dad, a couple of those people in your meeting seemed pretty hot on the idea that life was possible on the dark side of Mars."

Dr. Simmons snorted with unsuppressed laughter. "You seem to have forgotten your history. The Big Bang happened about seven billion years ago. By about four billion years ago most of the inner planets had formed and swept their orbits clear of debris from the explosion. In that period, Mars had an atmosphere and lots of water. About three and a half billion years ago, some cosmic event swept Mars' atmosphere away. What we see today is the aftermath of that."

Robert said, "What does that have to do with the dark side."

Dr. Simmons took a deep breath and asked, "You know that if you leave ice cubes in the tray for more than a week, the cubes will shrink. Did you ever wonder where the water went?"

"Not seriously enough to think about it."

"Well. It's too cold to melt, so it simply evaporated directly from solid to vapor by a process known as sublimation."

"Oh, my. That means the dark side could be devoid of water, too."

"It most certainly does."

Dr. Simmons rose and took his glasses and the now empty carafe to the sink.

Robert followed and as they put the glassware in the dishwasher, he turned to his father with a puzzled look. "Does this mean what I think it means?"

"To me, this smells like a hoax. Tomorrow I'll tell the group what I think and we'll see what comes of it. Good night Robert."

How Green Was That Probe?
Chapter Four
Submitted by Kent Humpal

The next morning, entering the Conference Room is Dr. Simmons. "Gentlemen, I have been thinking this event over all night. Actually I haven't slept since the Zoom meeting. I have discussed things with my son for a legal input, discussed things with Dr. Chagrin to clarify the order of the incident, and discussed things with Ron Sebolt, as he was the principal witness and recorder from the beginning.

"I and the other members of the project can and will vouch for Ron's devotion and integrity. Now we must come to a decision on how to proceed. First, was it real or a hoax? I know there are doubts and certainly questions about what we witnessed. So, speak out everyone, anyone?"

"I'll start," replied Dr. Chargin. "Like you I couldn't think about anything else last night. Ronnie and I spent the hours till dawn going over the data, both visual and oral. We could find nothing odd or unusual in our reception or recording equipment."

Ronnie broke in. "We checked and re-checked everything and everything seemed normal with the equipment. There is no evidence of a tampering or hack job that we could find. I'm pretty up to date on what can be done by other agencies, by foreign hackers, or by governments who are constantly evolving their methods, searching for information, useful or not. We can't consider it all but so far there is no evidence. It should be checked by experts, possibly by some Federal Agency as well."

Juan Fujimoto signaled that he had something to offer. "As you can probably surmise, the university would like to own this project and for the interesting occurrence to be kept as quiet as possible. They accept that only government agencies working with you should be informed, but they wish that it be kept from the media as much as possible.

"Unfortunately, the agencies and research groups you have already contacted in other countries cannot be controlled. We can only hope they will be discrete in their releases. However there have been leaks and speculations seen on the internet all ready."

Dr. Simmons, looking and sounding exhausted, began giving some directions to the group. "Mr. Sebolt and Ron please contact as many of the search and screening groups as you can. Ask the Federal Agency for help. They have whole departments for this. Check with the private group searching for extraterrestrial signals—you know the Institute for Extraterrestrial message reception and communications.

They call themselves IETMRC. They are a bit weird but they have some good sources. Check the dish, University of California Radio Telescopes, at Hot Creek USA, Satellite Monitoring system. Send the visual to NASA to verify that it was Gordon Scott in that room."

Dr. Simmons greeted his team the next day. "I see we have some new members joining us. Gentlemen, ladies, will you introduce yourselves please."

"I'm Colonel James Forth, U.S. Army, now posted to the new Space Force. I'm to give you all the help I can. I have a little information to give you at this time. We are primarily a defense unit."

"I represent NASA," replied the next person. I'm Dr. Kamala Gupta. We have no information on this situation yet. We are scanning all signals from our stations and will forward to you any pertinent information. At this time we cannot confirm the incident. We are highly skeptical of the validity of the image of Gordon Scott, however."

"I was invited by Dr. Chargin, Supervisor of IETMRT, says Dr. Meara ODonal. We have never received a transmission of yours. Most of our work deals with clots, electronic bursts, and what can be considered to be a magnetic signal from space. We do have a lot of experience with fake transmissions, however."

"Member of World Health Organization, U.S. Liaison, and PhD in Viral Transmissions, I was sent here to see if there was any connection with the virus Laguna Virus—39. I'm Frederick Douglas King at your service, sir."

"Well, we don't have much information to give to you all at present," said Dr. Simmons. "You're welcome to look over the transmissions, with Colonel Forth's okay, of course. We have reached out to research teams around the world working on similar projects, but nothing of note has been relayed to us yet. Dr. Chargin, do you have anything to add?"

"I have been conferring with many of our fellow agencies, even those controlled by hostile governments. They have been putting out statements on their websites. These are controlled, but there are ways you can talk to them that are unmonitored. They are pretty forthright, and they have nothing. Officially the North Koreans and Iranians are claiming that a U.S. plot to allow our government to increase surveillance of their space and nuclear programs is under way. In other words—weapons and missile sites. They are asking for the UN to intervene, and of course are threatening retaliation against our allies.

"What about China and Russia?" asked Colonel Forth.

Dr. Chargin, checking his screen, scrolled down and replied. "They both have denied having knowledge of the event, but now each country is claiming credit for getting the transmissions first and keeping it secret to avoid a world-wide panic. China is understandable as they never forget and they still resent the China Flu thing from the year 2019. Russia still resents their inability to regain their empire during Putin's 20 year reign and the turmoil following his death."

"Dr. Simmons, maybe we should let them take credit and take the world response, while we keep working on it," responded Colonel Forth.

Dr. Simmons, speaking to Ronnie. "Has there been any more visual or audio intercepts or any reports?"

"Nothing, Sir," replied Ronnie, scanning the dark screens and checking the audio recorders. "It's mostly static and deep space visuals. Not even a blip."

Dr. Simmons turned to the group and spoke. "As the leader of this project I need to direct our next moves. What we experienced is unexpected. Before I make decisions I need your input and advice. Our project was deep space research on Mars and its moon or moons. We have been side tracked by two things. One is tracking the origin of the Laguna Virus—39. Is it coming from Outer Space and is it directed by a sentient source? Secondly was the visual and audio transmission real or a fraud?

"If it was real, was it an intentional or accidental reception? We are faced with a choice. Do we continue with our original research or do we incorporate the new event into our studies. Or do we turn them over to other agencies to investigate. Think it over and give me your thoughts tomorrow. It will not be a one person decision."

How Green Was That Probe?

Chapter Five
Submitted by Virginia Braxton

It was now the fourth day since the green men had been seen on the Mars visual channel. The news was out, and it had spread even faster than the Laguna virus, but at least the tanks had been withdrawn from campus, and the demonstrations over the threat to academic freedom had fallen flat. The air was still filled, however, with rampant speculation as to the sources of the virus and the green men transmission.

A grim faced and exhausted Dr. Simmons called the Zoom conference to order. "Before we start our major business, gentlemen, there are a few matters to clear up.

"First of all, the Campus police determined that the fire was caused by an irresponsible student with a firecracker—a stupid act in a fire season—and they have turned the person responsible over to the appropriate authorities. We have run tests on our equipment and have not found any damage, however.

"Secondly, I'd like to introduce Dr. Bronson of NOAA. He is here to make available to the World Health Organization and any other agency needing it, his agency's extensive knowledge and data tracking capabilities on wind directions and speeds and their possible impact on the virus spread." Dr. Bronson nodded at the camera.

"Thirdly, I was not able to rid myself of the suspicion that down the hill somewhere on campus, in the basement of some frat house, there were a bunch of guys who started by rolling around on the floor helpless with laughter at the success of the hack they'd pulled off.

"About the time the tanks came onto the campus they realized things were out of hand, but they were scared, and did not know how to stop the onslaught of events. I made some discrete inquiries, and my hunch proved accurate. Incidentally, they had Photoshopped the Scott image from one of the photos published when he was lost.

"The national office of that fraternity has been informed that the fraternity is no longer welcome on campus, and despite their parents' protests, the hacking brothers have been conscripted and shipped to a bunker in Roswell, copiously supplied with beer and pizza."

"What if they're vegans?" someone interrupted.

"Then they can survive on corn and prickly pears," Simmons continued, "and they have superb equipment.

"They have been instructed to find a way to detect when one of the space balls enters our atmosphere and find a way to contain and neutralize it. They have been ordered to share any ideas or data they come up with. I suspect that they will be able to build up cordial working relationships with all the parties involved, especially IETMRC. They have now become our colleagues in fighting the virus. Clearly they are very bright, and their unconventional thinking habits may be an advantage to us.

"Now to review serious business—we need to discuss the spread of the virus. When we winnow out speculation," Simmons continued, "we have very few facts about the virus. What is especially problematic is that some of what we would consider as facts are not logically compatible with other seemingly correct facts. One possible reason may be that both the containers the virus arrives in and the virus itself easily transforms itself to adapt to different environments. If so, making generalizations leading to scientific conclusions may be virtually impossible.

In other words, our scientific binary thinking may not work on our current problem, leaving us adrift. That idea is devastating. Our way of thinking has worked for the last 400 years as far as I can tell, and I personally don't know any other way to think. But it is all we have to work with.

"I know I promised that our decision would not be mine alone, but here is what I would recommend. In front of you is a list of the seven most powerful computers I know of and their host institutions. I suggest we feed all the sightings of virus containers with their attached data on surrounding environments into those computers. Then we can have each computer, using the algorithms developed by the host institution, look for mini patterns or clusters. After that we can compare the results between computers. If several computers come up with the same clusters, we can start analyzing each cluster individually.

"Each subset may suggest its own methods of amelioration and prevention, so we will probably have to go at this virus from a lot of fronts simultaneously.

"Does anyone have anything to add?" There was silence.

"Well, time to get to work. Everyone, keep your minds nimble but don't contaminate your data with speculation. In the meantime, remember: wear masks, wash your hands, and keep your social distance."

Made in the USA
Coppell, TX
08 November 2020